D1599511

Fascinating
Experiments in
PHYSICS

Fascinating Experiments in PHYSICS

by François Cherrier

Technical Consultant: Maurice Finot, Professor of Chemistry and Physics

STERLING PUBLISHING CO., INC. NEW YORK
Oak Tree Press Co., Ltd. London & Sydney

Other Books of Interest

Translated by E. W. Egan

Adapted by Dennis Schuchman

Photographs and layout by the author

25431
Second Printing, 1979

Copyright © 1978 by Sterling Publishing Co., Inc.
   Two Park Avenue, New York, N.Y. 10016
Original edition of this book was published in France under the title "Expériences de Physique
   Amusante" © 1975 by Librarie Hachette, Paris.
Distributed in Australia by Oak Tree Press Co., Ltd.,
   P.O. Box J34, Brickfield Hill, Sydney 2000, N.S.W.
Distributed in the United Kingdom by Ward Lock Ltd., 116 Baker Street, London, W.1
Manufactured in the United States of America
All rights reserved
Library of Congress Catalog Card No.: 78-57789
Sterling ISBN 0-8069-3104-3 Trade   Oak Tree 7061-2596-7
                3105-1 Library

Contents

A word about these experiments

Archimedes asked for a fulcrum and a lever to move the world. Since then physics has seen some extraordinary developments. Without physics there would be no steam engines or automobile engines, no jet planes, no electricity, no trips to the moon.

Of course, this book is not going to teach you how to construct an interplanetary rocket! But the experiments that you will find here and carry out with items at your disposal (magnets, cardboard, plastic pipes, bottles, plastic foam, elastic bands, etc.) will take you into an equally fascinating world.

Would you like to create a rainbow? A glass of water and a blank sheet of paper will do it. Would you like to see objects reflected infinitely? Two mirrors carefully placed will do the trick. Would you like to "see" sound waves? The top of a plastic bottle and an elastic membrane are all it takes. Would you like to follow the trajectory of drops of water in a fountain? A stroboscope, very simple to construct, will give you the means.

Nor is that all there is. The simple and concrete explanations in this spendidly illustrated book will stimulate you to make solar furnaces, bathyscaphes, steam turbines . . .

It's up to you to choose. Every one of the marvels you will create will amaze you. From here on you are in a research laboratory.

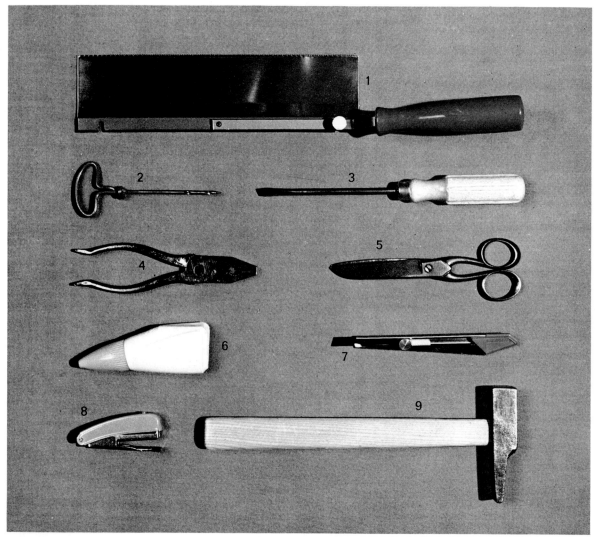

Tools (above): 1. back saw 2. gimlet 3. screwdriver 4. box pliers 5. ordinary scissors 6. wood glue 7. sharp knife 8. small stapler 9. hammer

Supplies and main accessories (opposite page): 1. wooden spools 2. plastic-coated steel clothespins 3. angle irons 4. flexible plastic tubing 5. insulated wire 6. copper wire 7. steel knitting needles with plastic casings 8. light bulbs 9. soft plastic pipette bottle 10. magnet from door latch 11. steel ball bearings.

Supplies and tools

Small magnets can be removed from magnetic locks installed on cabinet doors. The plastic housing containing the magnet can be eased out of the lock with a screwdriver. You can also find magnets in old loudspeakers, but these are circular. Magnets have two surfaces, generally at the ends, that attract iron and steel: these are the north and south poles. They attract each other (when north and south are face to face) or repel each other (when north faces north, or south, south).

Iron filings can be obtained from a mechanic. They consist of little grains of iron that fall off when the metal is filed.

Steel balls can be obtained from worn-out ball bearings from a mechanic or metalwork shop. With a cold chisel, split a few rivets and remove the metal channel holding the balls.

For a *punch*, file the end of a thick metal tube so as to

obtain a chamfered cutting edge formed by the interior circumference of the tube.

Expanded polystyrene (Styrofoam®) is the plastic foam material used to make ice containers. You can get it from various packing materials. Glue it with wood glue.

You can find *flexible tubing* at an aquarium supply store or from television antenna cables (the lining is a plastic tube).

Small rigid tubes come from lollipop sticks or the casing of plastic-covered steel knitting needles: cut the casing near the head of the needle with a knife and remove it from the steel core.

Angle irons are very useful in these experiments. Small ones can be sawed from longer lengths of angle iron.

Magnifying mirrors are available everywhere that grooming accessories and toilet articles are sold. To remove them from their frames, remove the small screw on the rim and pull the two ends apart with a sideways motion.

Some advice

☐ Have your wood cut to the desired dimensions at the timber supply store. It is important to have precision-cut boards to mount your uprights on.

☐ To install an upright on a board, make a hole in the board that a screw can easily pass through. Widen the edge of the hole on the underside of the board to make room for the head of the screw. Make a small preliminary hole in the upright with an awl. Daub the base of the upright with glue and put the screw into the upright through the board.

☐ Pierce holes in the boards and sticks with a small hand drill, and if needed, enlarge the hole with a rat-tail file. Pierce corks with an awl and enlarge the hole with a rat-tail file. For all these holes you can use a nail whose tip has been made red hot over a gas flame. Hold the nail firmly with a pair of pliers. (All the holes shown in the photos were made in this way.)

☐ If you are especially interested in any of the subjects in this book or if you have any questions, don't hesitate to refer to physics text books or to ask your teacher.

Note: In order for certain liquids to show up well in the photos, we have added a little fluorescein for a yellow-green tint. This substance is not easy to obtain, but a bit of mercurochrome will give almost the same result and a greenish-orange tint.

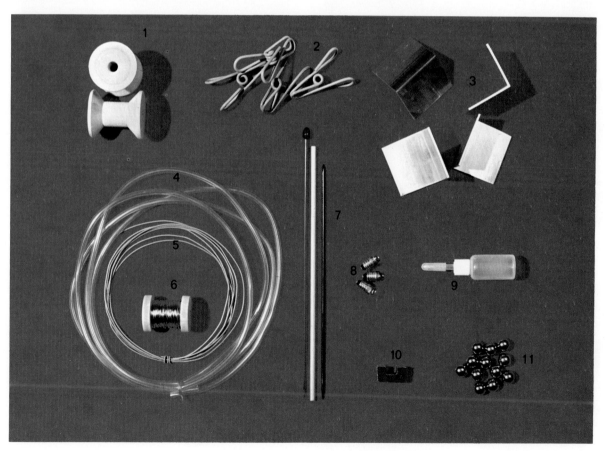

magnets

Three-dimensional magnetism

Supplies: liquid Vaseline®; iron powder or filings; jar with a lid; small magnet; wire; pencil.

Put a layer of iron powder 0.5 cm thick in the bottom of the jar, then fill the jar with Vaseline®. Close it and shake until well mixed.

Suspend the magnet from the pencil with wire. Open the jar and immediately dip the magnet into it, letting the pencil rest on the rim of the jar. Do not touch anything until the liquid becomes clear again. You will then see that the powder reproduces all the lines of force making up the magnetic field, as shown in the photo on the opposite page.

Spectral pictures

Supplies: piece of plastic foam or thick corrugated cardboard; small magnets; iron powder in a shaker —fill a can with iron powder, cover it with paper perforated with pinholes and held in place with an elastic band; drawing paper; four thumbtacks; photo-sensitive solution—dissolve 10 grams of iron ammonium citrate (from the pharmacist) in 50 cm³ of water, then dissolve 5 grams of potassium ferricyanide in 50 cm³ of water, and mix the two solutions in the dark.

In dim light, swab the drawing paper with the solution and let it dry. In the middle of the plastic foam board, cut out a niche for the magnet and insert it all the way in, flush with the surface. Place the sensitized paper over it, held in place by four thumbtacks. Sprinkle the iron powder over the entire surface of the paper. Expose it to direct sunlight for 15 minutes, then rinse the sheet under running water for 20 minutes until the powder is removed. Let it dry. Photo 2 shows what you will get with a circular magnet. (Photo 3 shows you a similar image obtained in this case in a bath of oil: the magnet is placed under a flat receptacle.) Other examples, with one or two magnets, appear on page 14. The iron filings will form the same patterns without the photosensitive solution or exposure to sunlight, but you will not obtain a lasting image.

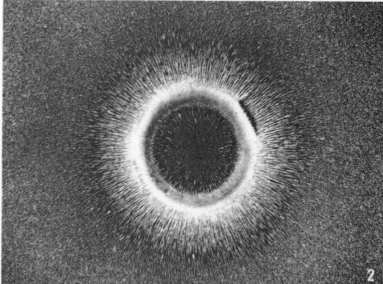

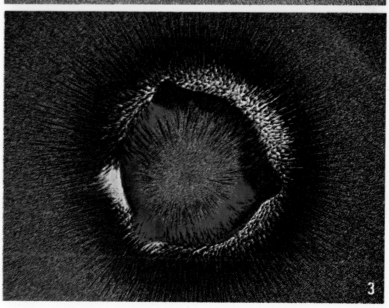

13

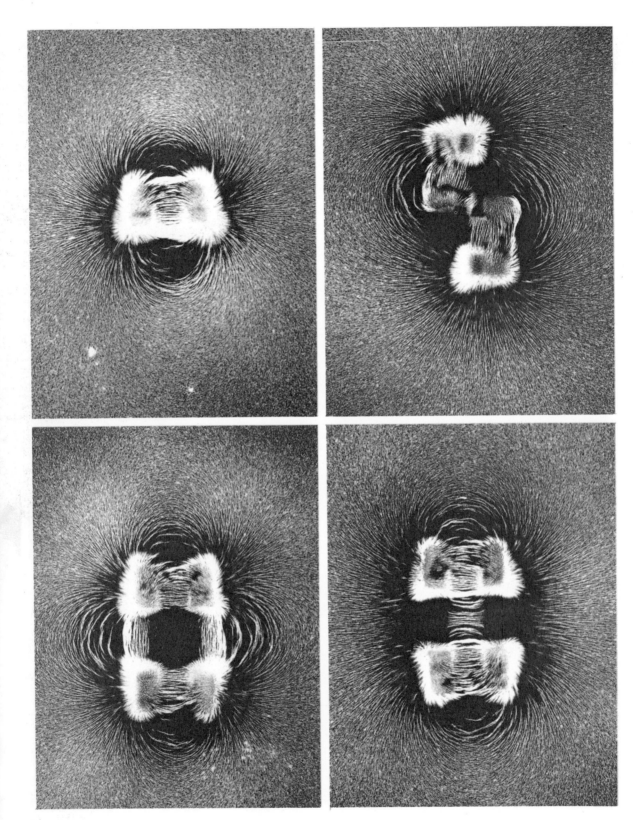

14

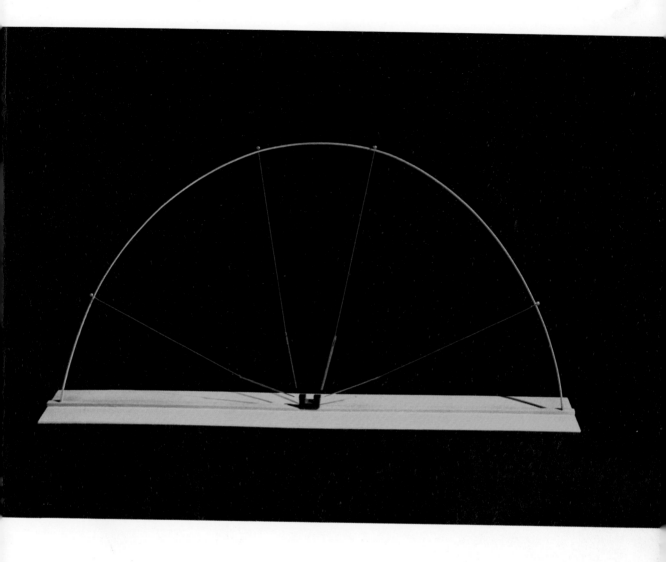

Threads stretched in space

Supplies: small magnet; 10 x 60 x 0.5-cm plywood board; strip of flexible wood 90 cm long; thread; sewing needles; pins; double-coated adhesive tape.

Make a notch at each end of the board and insert the ends of the wood strip after dipping them in glue. Make holes along the wood strip and pass threaded needles through them so that the threads extend 10 cm beyond the holes. In the middle of the board, attach the magnet with adhesive tape or glue. Adjust the threads carefully so that the tips of the needles are attracted to the magnet without touching it. Then fix the thread in the holes with pins. If your magnet is not too strong, magnetize each needle by rubbing it in one direction with one pole of the magnet. Arrange as shown above.

A challenge to gravity (page 16)

Supplies: two large balls of plastic foam (crafts supply shops have them); two small magnets from a door latch; copper wire; thumbtacks; thread.

Using a knife, dig a niche for a magnet in each ball, then lodge the magnet in it so that it is flush with the surface. Loop the wire around the magnet and pass it all the way through the ball. At the other end make a loop out of the wire and attach a thread to it (see Drawing A, page 16). Hang one of the balls from the ceiling, and directly under it place a heavy book on the floor to hold down the thread of the other ball. Take this ball and bring it near the one hanging from the ceiling until the magnetic attraction balances its weight and holds it in the air. Remove the book and anchor the thread to the floor with a push-pin or thumbtack.

15

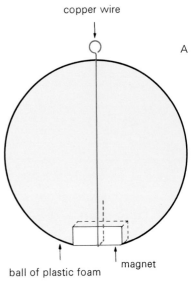

copper wire

A

ball of plastic foam   magnet

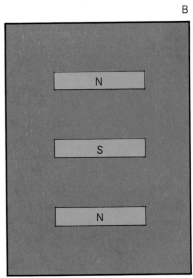

B

N

S

N

aluminum sheet

C

piece of plastic foam   magnet

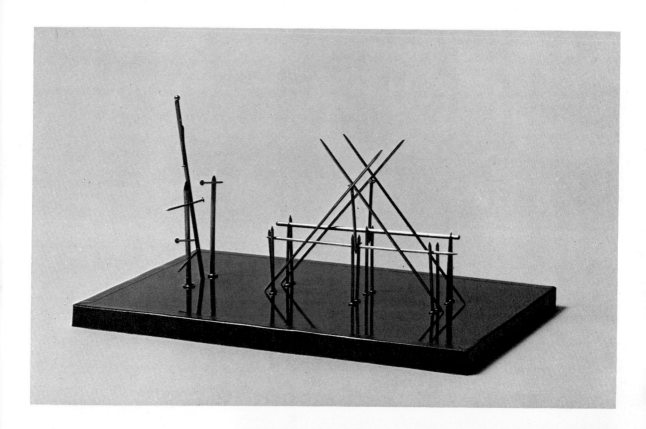

Magnetic tray

Supplies: three flat magnets (poles on the main faces); plastic foam board and piece of aluminum of the same size; adhesive tape; metal rods; nails.

Cut niches for the three magnets in the plastic foam board and fit them in, alternating the poles: North, South, North (on the top). Each pole must be able to attract the pole of the magnet next to it (Drawing B). Join the plastic foam board and the aluminum sheet with adhesive tape. Using steel knitting needles, nails, etc., you can make interesting constructions like the one above.

Improvised compass

Supplies: jar with a plastic lid; silk thread; bar magnet (poles at the ends).

Hang the magnet by the silk thread and pass the thread through a hole worked in the lid of the jar and knot the thread. Place the magnet in the jar and close the lid. The magnet will assume a north-south orientation. Knowing that the sun rises in the east, you can then adjust your compass.

Magnetic sculptures

Supplies: steel balls of different sizes salvaged from scrap ball bearings (available from a mechanic's shop); small magnets from door latches or circular magnets from an old loudspeaker; pieces of wood; iron filings.

Here are four examples of sculptures that are easy to make and whose form you can change at will.

At the left, a circular magnet, held by a nail on a painted wood support, is covered with balls of different sizes. Above, small magnets attached to pieces of wood make clusters of steel balls appear to flow. At right, iron fillings have been spilled over two magnets, causing this bizarre seated figure to appear. On page 11, straight magnets are assembled on top of one another and covered with balls and nails. Now it's up to you to find other ideas for magnetic sculptures.

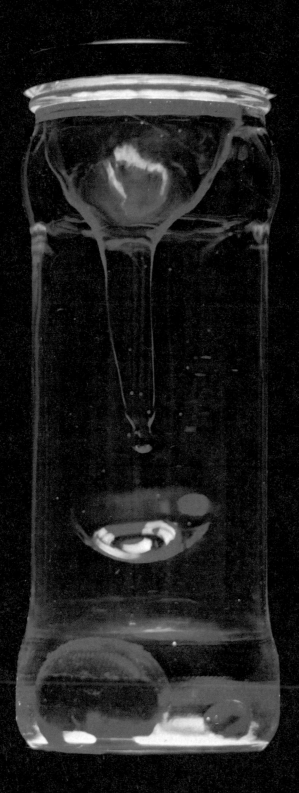

fluids

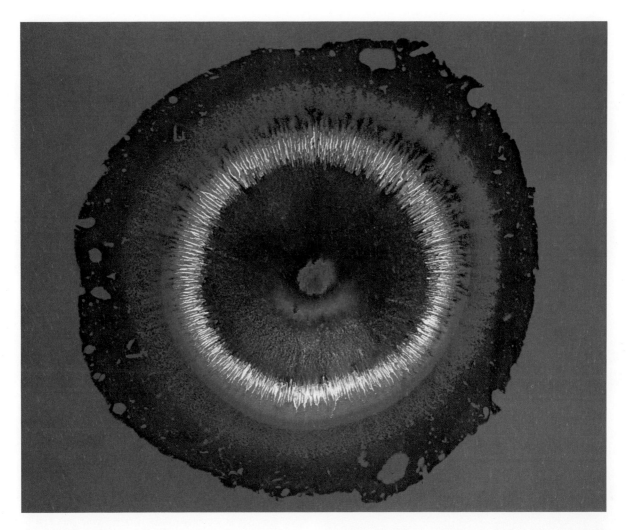

Franklin boiling (opposite page)

or how to boil water with cold water

Supplies: Pyrex® boiling flask with rubber stopper; alcohol lamp; wire tripod; large beaker (see Photo 2); iron wire.

Make an iron wire support to hold the flask upside down in the beaker. Half fill the flask with water and bring it to a boil, uncovered, with the alcohol lamp (Photo 1). Using a dish towel, remove the jar from the heat and quickly seal it tight—the bubbling stops. Turn the flask upside down in the beaker and pour cold water on it—the water starts to boil again (Photo 2).

It is essential that the flask be removed from the heat before it is stoppered. A round-bottomed flask should be used as an additional safety measure and proper eye protection should be provided. This experiment should be conducted under a teacher's supervision.

☐ When the flask is stoppered, it contains hot water and water vapor which has partially expelled the air from the jar. By cooling the sides of the jar, the vapor is changed into drops of water, so that the space above the water is left practically empty; at this point the pressure in the jar is very low. The lower the pressure, the lower the boiling point of the water. That's why water boils at a lower temperature in the mountains where the air pressure is lower than at sea level.

Black sun (above)

or the struggle of a drop of ink in a sea of gouache

Supplies: glass plate; gouache paint; India ink.

Heavily dilute the gouache and spread it evenly over the glass. Drop a spot of India ink in the middle of it. Immediately, the gouache recoils, as though in battle. The ink advances and breaks into an attractive black "sunburst."

☐ This is a mixture of liquids of different natures: the ink dissolves slowly in the gouache, causing a progressive movement that forms delicate branchlike patterns.

Liquid layers

or how to superimpose liquids without mixing them

Supplies: tall narrow jar; glycerine and liquid paraffin (from the pharmacist); pure alcohol; water; food colorings (from supermarket, etc.).

Pour tinted glycerine, then water very slowly down the side of the jar. Now pour tinted liquid paraffin in the same way, then tinted alcohol. The different liquids lie one on top of the other without mixing.

☐ These liquids have different densities: the glycerine is heavier than water; the paraffin is lighter than the water, and the alcohol is lighter than the paraffin.

Siphon water jet

or how atmospheric pressure makes siphons work

Supplies: small jar; cork with two holes pierced through it; medicine dropper; one tube 1 m long and one 20 cm long, both 5 mm in diameter; two containers; candle; ink; (the stand shown in the photo is not essential).

Fit the cork into the jar. Push the medicine dropper through one of the holes until it is halfway into the jar. Attach the 20-cm tube to it. Insert the 1-m tube until its tip is flush with the inside surface of the cork. Remove the cork, put the jar on the table and half fill it with water.

Recork it firmly and seal it by pouring melted candle wax over it. Fill one container with water (tinted with ink) and place it on the table with the end of the shorter tube in it. Put the end of the long tube in an empty container placed on the floor. Now turn the jar upside down: a jet of water spurts out of the tube (medicine dropper) into the jar and continues to spurt as long as there is water in the container.

☐ As the water in the jar flows through the long tube the pressure in the jar decreases. The decrease in pressure is strong enough to suck up the water through the short tube and cause a jet of water to spurt.

Sleight-of-hand trick

or how to invert a glass full of water without spilling a drop

Supplies: three identical glasses; sheet of paper.

Fill the first glass with water up to the top. Place a sheet of paper over it and invert it carefully, holding the paper with the other hand. Take your hand away and place the glass on the table. Then, lifting the glass very slightly, pull the paper away.

Now proceed in the same way with another glass, but this time placing it on another glass full of water. Make sure that the edges coincide perfectly before pulling the paper away.

☐ Atmospheric pressure holds the water in the inverted glasses.

Magic glasses

Supplies: two identical glasses; a small stemmed glass; cotton yarn (candle wicks); plate; alcohol tinted with mercurochrome.

Place the two glasses, filled with water, on the plate, one inverted over the other, as described above. Place the stemmed glass on top of them, filled with tinted alcohol. Hang the wicks over the rim. Drops of alcohol fall from the wicks upon the outside of the inverted glass, penetrate the crack between the two glasses, and then rise in the inverted glass (photos on opposite page).

☐ The alcohol moves by capillary action down the wicks, and, as it is lighter than water, it rises in the inverted glass.

26

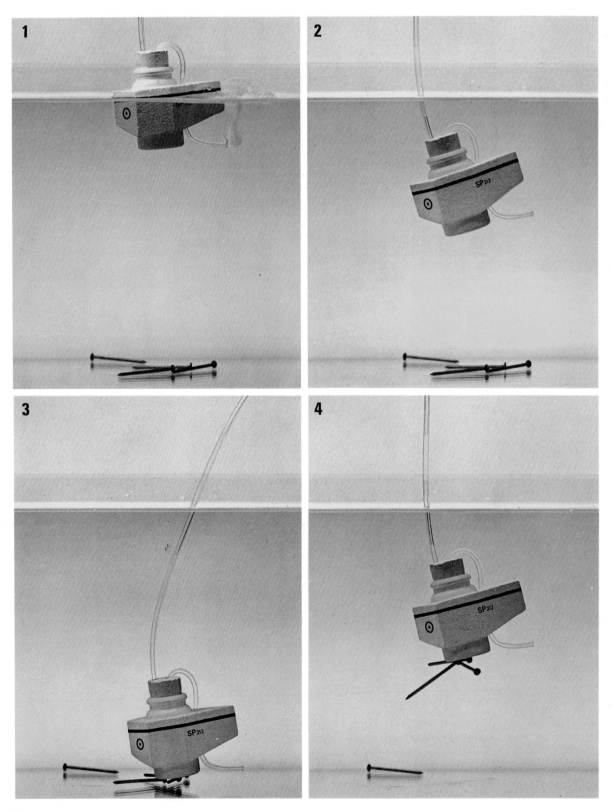

28

The bathyscaph

Supplies: 24-cm³ medicine bottle (3 cm in diameter); cork; two lengths of flexible tubing; magnet from door latch; piece of plastic foam; vinyl paint.

Using a sharp knife, cut out the body of the bathyscaph from the plastic foam as shown in Drawings A and B. Fit the cork to the mouth of the bottle, and pierce two holes of the diameter of the pipes using an awl or a rat-tail file. Place a magnet in the bottle, cork the bottle, and wedge it into the body of the bathyscaph. Form the siphon by curving the tip of one tube by immersing it in very hot water and holding it in a curved position for a short time. Stick the other tip into the body of the bathyscaph, then through one of the holes in the cork all the way to the bottom of the bottle. The outer part of the siphon should extend to the bottom of the bottle (Drawing C).

Insert a tube 50 cm long into the other hole so that the tip is flush with the bottom surface of the cork. If the water does not reach the black water line when the bathyscaph is placed in water, add several bits of lead to the bottle. If the bathyscaph sinks, use a smaller magnet. Paint the assembly any way you like.

Place the bathyscaph in water and blow air through the long pipe. The air escapes to the rear, which gives forward thrust to the vessel (like a jet plane); it moves across the surface (Photo 1). Suck a little air through the pipe—the water enters the bottle through the siphon, the bottle becomes heavier and it starts to sink (Photo 2). When the bathyscaph reaches the bottom it picks up wreckage (nails) thanks to its magnet (Photo 3). Blow into the pipe again—water is expelled through the siphon, the bathyscaph becomes lighter and rises to the surface (Photo 4).

☐ A real bathyscaph contains a liquid lighter than water and carries a supply of iron shot that it dumps in order to get back up.

Variation: Drawing D is a simplified version without a hull.

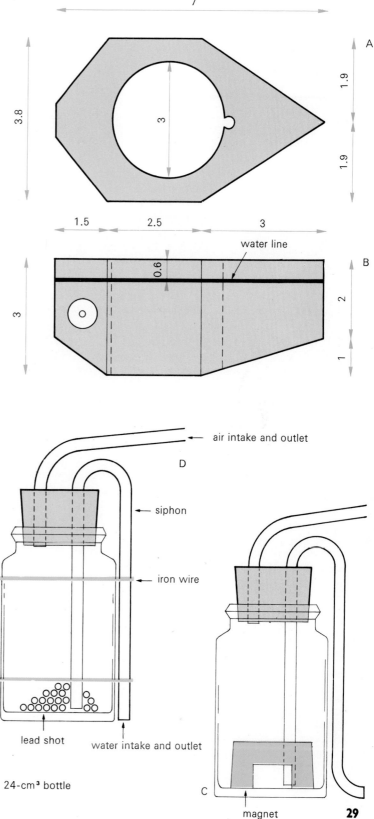

water line

air intake and outlet

siphon

iron wire

lead shot

water intake and outlet

24-cm³ bottle

magnet

Sphere of oil

or the form taken by a liquid free to spread

Supplies: Vaseline® oil (pharmacy); fuel alcohol (housewares shop); glass jar; coloring for oil (oil paint, all-purpose paint coloring, artist's pigment, liquid or powdered, etc.); soft plastic medicine-dropper bottle; spoon.

Fill the jar ¾ full with alcohol and add a drop of Vaseline® oil: it sinks to the bottom. Add a little water, gradually, until the drop of oil rises to the middle of the jar—the density of the water-alcohol mixture is then equal to that of the oil. Delicately mix the water and alcohol with a small spoon.

Now pour some more oil into the medicine-dropper bottle and color it slightly. Then gently, but without stopping, pour the oil carefully into the water-alcohol mixture by squeezing the bottle flush with the surface: a sphere then forms in the middle of the jar. If it floats too high, add some alcohol; if it is too low, add water.

☐ The phenomenon known as surface tension gives the mass of oil the form of a perfect sphere in a liquid of the same density.

Variation (photo opposite page): Pour small quantities of different-colored oil delicately on the surface of alcohol-water mixture.

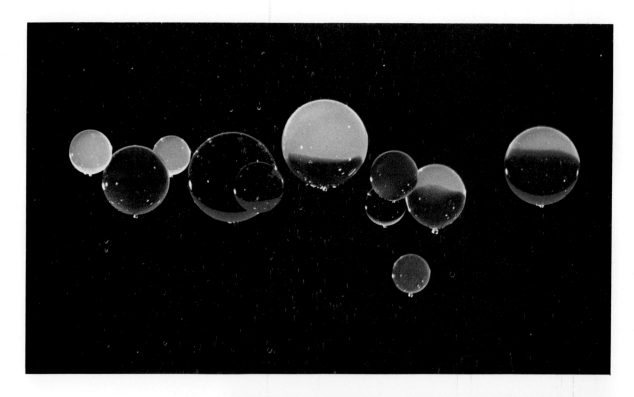

Capillarity

or how water rises spontaneously in a narrow vessel

Supplies: two small glass plates of equal size; a match; elastic bands; a dish; ink or mercurochrome.

Put a little water in the dish and color it with ink or mercurochrome. Place the match between the two glass plates and hold them together with an elastic band. The match should be at one end of the plates (see photo at right). Place this assembly on the plate and hold it in place with an elastic band. Bit by bit the water will rise between the two plates and form a graceful curve whose maximum height will be at the point where the plates are closest together.

☐ The smaller the space between the two plates, the higher the water will rise. This phenomenon is called capillarity.

Cartesian divers

Supplies: large, wide-mouthed jar with cork; small, soft plastic squeeze-bottles with nozzles; lead or solder wire; flexible tubing; soft plastic squeeze-bottle, about 125 cm³ in volume; paint.

Fill the jar with water to a height about 2 cm from the cork. Weight the little bottles by twisting lead wire around the ends: this ballast should keep them immersed to ¾ of their height. Paint faces on the divers. Fill each bottle with water to the point where they are completely immersed but still float at the top of the jar. If they sink to the bottom, expel the water drop by drop until they float properly. Pierce a hole in the cork and insert the tube as far as the under-surface of the cork. Connect the other end of the tube to the squeeze-bottle. Put the cork firmly in place and squeeze the bottle. The divers sink. Stop squeezing and they rise.

☐ When you exert pressure on the squeeze-bottle, the air between the cork and the suface of the water is compressed. The water transmits this pressure to the air contained within the divers, which is then compressed. Water then enters the divers, their weight increases and they sink. When you stop squeezing the bottle, water is expelled from the divers and they rise.

Variation: Stretch a piece of rubber sheeting over the mouth of the jar (see drawing below). When you press on this membrane, the divers sink.

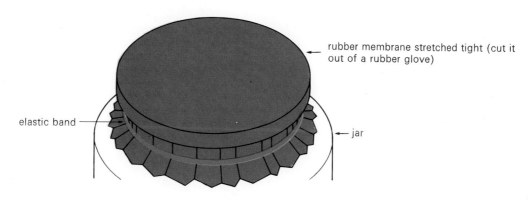

elastic band

rubber membrane stretched tight (cut it out of a rubber glove)

jar

mirrors

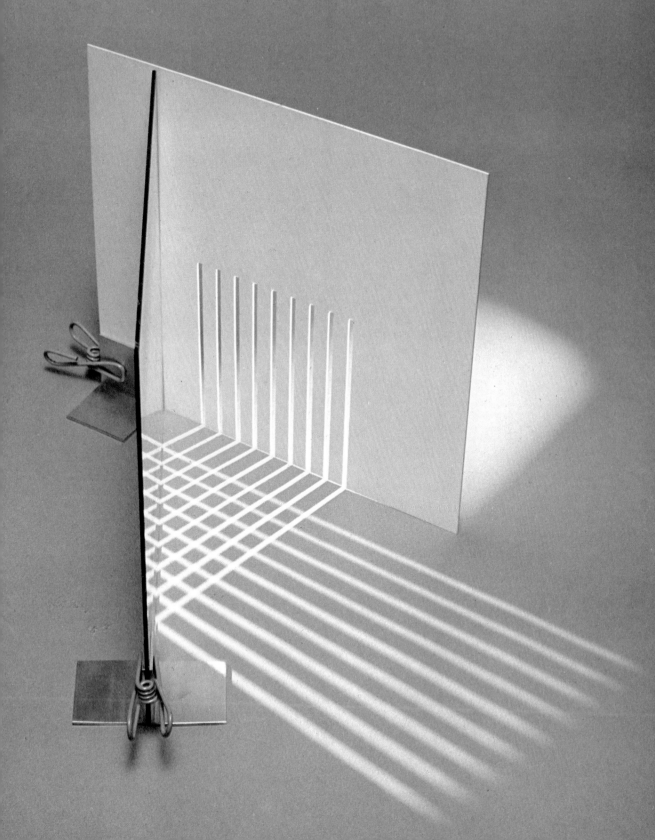

An infinity of flowers

Supplies: two mirrors; four small angle irons; clip-type clothespins.

With a penknife, scrape a round patch about 1 cm in diameter from the silvering in the middle of the back of one mirror. Using the clothespins, attach the angle irons to the base of each mirror so that it will stand up. Set the mirrors parallel to each other, with the reflecting surfaces facing one another. Place an object in the middle, then peep through the little hole (Drawing A). The object will be reproduced infinitely.

Truth mirror

or how to see yourself as others see you

Supplies: two mirrors; one angle iron; clip-type clothespins.

Make a right angle with the two mirrors (Drawing B), assembling them with the aid of an angle iron held by two clothespins. Place an alarm clock or a written message in front of them. You will then be surprised to find that you can read normally in the angle of the two mirrors: the image is not a "mirror" image. If you look at yourself you will see your own image in the same spot, the way you look to others.

Play of sunbeams

or how a mirror sends back images (photo on page 35)

Supplies: a mirror; four angle irons; clothespins; a large comb or a piece of cardboard cut out in a comb-like pattern.

Place the cardboard cutout facing the sunlight or an electric lamp (oblique lighting). Place a mirror at an angle to the cardboard, then turn it slightly. You will see on the table that the light is always reflected from the mirror at an angle equal to that at which it strikes it.

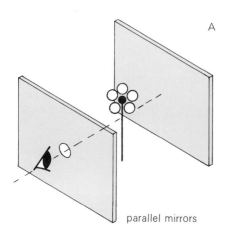

A

parallel mirrors

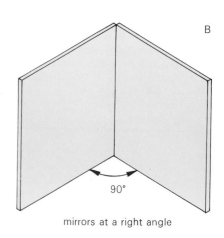

B

90°

mirrors at a right angle

Burning mirror

or how to increase the radiation of the sun enough to ignite paper

Supplies: concave spherical mirror (magnifying mirror); sheet of paper.

Turn the mirror towards the sun: the optical axis, that is, the imaginary line originating in the middle of the mirror and perpendicular to it, must line up with the sunlight. Place a sheet of paper or a piece of soft wood between the mirror and the sun; then move the paper back and forth until you obtain the smallest possible point of light reflected on it. In a few moments the paper ignites.

☐ This very old experiment is the basis of solar furnaces. When the rays of the sun, parallel to the optic axis, reflect from the mirror, they all converge upon a single point (the focus) located in the focal plane. To see the progression of rays reflected by the mirror, put some smoke in their path (cigarette smoke, smoke from a freshly extinguished candle, etc.). You will distinctly see two cones form. The focus is situated where they meet. Not only is the light of the sun concentrated at this point, but also its heat, which is so strong it can even ignite a piece of wood. Therefore, never leave a magnifying mirror in direct sunlight, for it can ignite nearby objects when the sun is on its axis.

It is said that Archimedes set fire to the Roman fleet at Syracuse by using "burning mirrors" to direct the rays of the sun on the ships. In our time, the solar furnace at Odeillo in the Pyrenees, which is nothing but a large mirror, can obtain temperatures of over 3,000°C.

Solar furnace I

a quick, economical project

Supplies: an auto headlight reflector (from a junk dealer or mechanic); two strips of wood about 1 cm thick and about 3 cm longer than the radius of the headlight reflector; wooden board about 30 cm by 15 cm; pins; cork; Pyrex® tube; wood screws; metal washers.

Bend back the edge of the headlight reflector at a right angle and punch two holes opposite each other in the bent rim. Insert a wood screw in each hole with a washer and attach the reflector to the wood strips. Attach the pieces of wood to the board. Insert a cork into the hole intended for the bulb of the headlight and stick four pins into it to hold a small glass tube at the proper height (see photo).

Aim the headlight towards the sun in such a way that all the rays of sunlight converge on the glass tube (strongly luminous point). When you have found the right spot, leave the furnace there. Put water in the tube. In a few moments the water will start to boil!

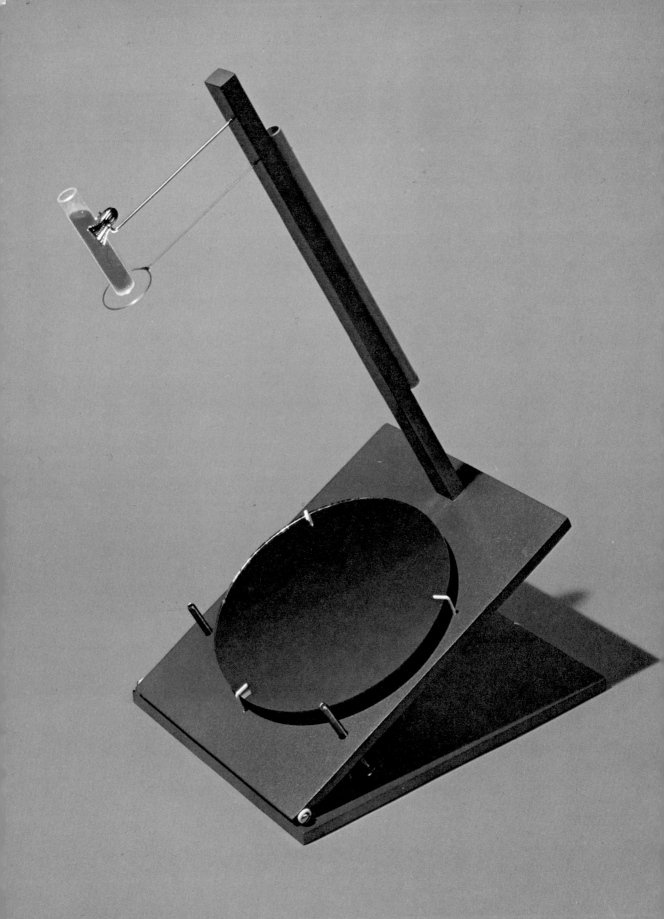

Solar furnace II

a powerful furnace with which you can boil water in a few seconds or run the steam turbine on page 42

Supplies (the numbers in parentheses refer to the picture below, to the text and to the drawing on page 42): two small boards measuring 1 cm thick, one 21 × 27 cm (1) and the other 19 × 27 cm (2); wooden stick measuring 1.5 × 1.5 × 36 cm (3); magnifying mirror 18 cm in diameter (4) removed from its frame; two round-head metal screws 7 cm long with nuts (5); metal knitting needle (6); small metal spring clamp (7) for holding dish cloths; piece of cellulose sponge (8); iron wire (9); three plastic-covered right-angle hooks (10); two plastic-covered screw-eyes (11); two round-head wood screws (12); small Pyrex®, copper or aluminum tube (13) with bottom part painted dull black; paint for heating fixtures; flat-head wood screw (see pages 8 and 9).

The photo below shows the solar furnace before assembly. The drawing on page 42 illustrates the construction details. Here are some additional hints to help you build it.

First determine the distance of the focus of the mirror. To do this, point the mirror towards the sun and put a metal strip on the axis between the mirror and the sun. Move the strip back and forth until you obtain the smallest point of light. Then measure the distance from the mirror to the strip. If it doesn't measure 29 cm, adjust the dimensions of the drawing to conform to the distance you find.

The holes for the screws (5) should be slightly wider than the screws. On the board (2) cut out the wood around each nut in order to embed the nut and hold it fast. Mark the place on the board (1) where the screw head is to go and cut the wood so that it fits in all the way. The base of the upright (3) must be sawed exactly at a right angle; check its perpendicularity to the board (2) with a T-square before screwing and gluing it in place.

Screw the two screw-eyes (11) in the corners of the board (1), 7 mm from the edge, then put the screws (12) that you will use to form the hinge through them. Now cut out a 4 cm-wide ring from the cellulose sponge. It should have a total diameter of 15 cm. With a pencil trace the contour of the mirror in the board (2). Place the sponge ring over it, then the mirror (the bottom of the mirror must not touch the board) and screw in the right-angle hooks at three equidistant points just outside the circle traced on the board. To make the holder for the tube (13), bend the end of the knitting needles (6) at a right angle and insert it into the joint of the little clamp (7), or wrap an iron wire around the needle and the tube (14). The wire ring indicating the focus (9) has a diameter of 3 cm and has a stem 10 cm long. To adjust the mirror, tip the plank (2) towards the sun by turning the screws (5). If the luminous spot is not exactly in the center of the ring below the bottom of the tube, adjust one or another of the angle hooks (10).

You can make an aimer with a tube 1 cm in diameter and 20 cm long, pierced all the way through by 2 nails and attached to the back of the upright on the main axis. The lower part of the tube is covered by a piece of clear adhesive tape (or of tracing paper). Your furnace will be adjusted when the sun illuminates the surface of the tape.

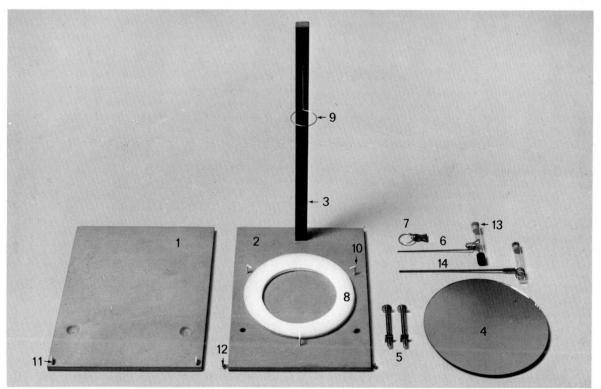

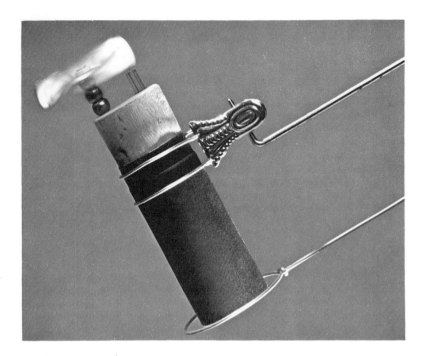

Steam turbine

operated by solar furnace II

Supplies: copper tube about 3 cm in diameter; cork; flat-head nail; beads; circle of tin plate or foil 3 cm in diameter; fine glass tube; brass wire; matte black paint for heating apparatus.

Paint the copper tube black. Pierce the cork and put the glass tube through it. It should be flush with the inside surface of the cork. Cut out the tin plate circle (as in "Hot-air mobiles" on page 87) and mount it on the cork with a nail and 2 or 3 beads. The blades should be close to the tip of the glass tube but not touching it. Make a double ring of brass wire around the copper tube that can be held by the clamp of the furnace. Fill the tube ⅔ with water. Cork and place in the clamp of the furnace and aim the furnace. In a few minutes the water boils, and steam comes out of the tube and makes the turbine spin.

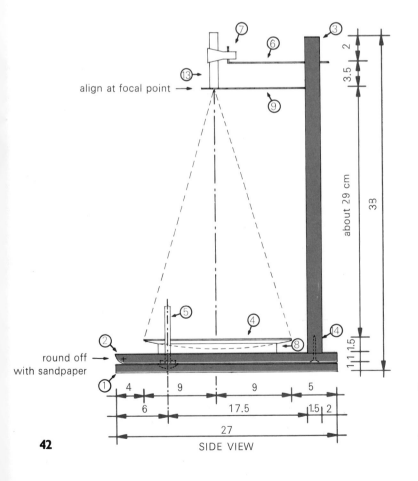

align at focal point →

round off with sandpaper →

SIDE VIEW

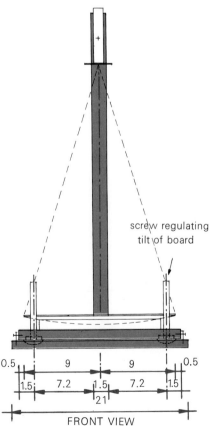

screw regulating tilt of board

about 29 cm

FRONT VIEW

42

Kaleidoscope

Supplies: two 12 cm × 4 cm mirrors; a piece of cardboard 12 cm × 4 cm; two elastic bands or adhesive tape; small scraps of colored paper; angle irons; clothespins.

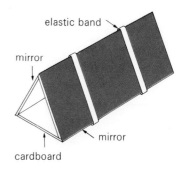

Arrange the two mirrors and the cardboard as shown in the drawing, holding them together with two elastic bands. Look through the axis of this prism at one end, and place the little scraps of colored paper on a sheet of white paper a few centimetres from the other end. You will see lovely images that change whenever you shift the scraps of colored paper. You can also, as seen below, place two mirrors so as to form a 60 degree angle on any kind of picture.

☐ The two mirrors forming a 60 degree angle do not give just two direct images of the object placed between them, but also give images of the images, or five images, plus the object itself. You can thus see a symmetrical hexagonal figure that is often very complex.

forces

Amazing marbles

the thousand-and-one phenomena of the propagation of shocks (photo above)

Supplies: board 22 × 32 × 1 cm; four sticks measuring 1.5 × 1.5 × 25 cm; four sticks measuring 2.4 cm in width and 0.7 cm in thickness, two of them 27 cm long and two 16 cm long; nine large steel balls; four wood screws; four small nails; strong thread; epoxy glue; wood glue; pure alcohol; pins.

Construct the framework as shown in the drawing on page 48. First put the four uprights in place on the base.

Their bottoms must be perfectly squared off. Check with T-square and level, and adjust with a very fine rasp if needed. Put holes in the spots on the base where the uprights are to go. Daub the ends of the uprights with glue and screw them in place with wood screws. Now install the cross pieces, beginning with the shorter ones. They should be flush with the tops of the uprights. Apply wood glue and hold each glued piece in place with two small nails. Finish the longer sides in the same way.

Clean the balls of all grease with pure alcohol and

place them on a piece of cardboard punched with holes as shown in Drawing B on page 48. Cut nine lengths of thread, each 50 cm long. Put a tiny dab of epoxy on the top of each ball, then carefully place the midpoint of a thread on each dab of glue. Add another drop of glue and let dry 48 hours without touching them.

On the upper surface of each of the long slats, carefully mark the spot where the threads are to go. Begin in the middle and mark off four dots on each side of the center mark. The distance between each dot should be equal to the diameter of each ball. If you do not know their diameter, measure it by placing one of them between the teeth of an adjustable wrench. Then make a groove as wide as the thread at each dot, perpendicular to the edge, using a blade or a small saw. Next place an alignment block 7 cm high and 17 cm long on the main axis of the base as shown in Drawing C on page 48. Place the thread holding a marble in two facing grooves letting the ball rest on the alignment block. Install the threads temporarily with pins stuck in the grooves. When all the balls are in place, make sure they are exactly in line, and put a dab of epoxy in each groove. Remove the pins when the glue is dry. Your installation is complete.

Take the first ball and then let it go. It strikes the others, but they remain immobile, except for the last one, which swings out. This one swings back and causes the first ball to swing out and this repeats itself for several minutes (Photo 1). Now take two balls—the result is the same except that this time the last two balls swing out (Photo 2). With three balls, three balls swing out from the other end (Photo 3). With four balls, only one, the middle ball, remains motionless (Photo 4). Many other combinations are possible—it's up to you to work them out.

☐ When the ball is released it imparts a force on the second ball, which transmits the impulse to the other balls without displacing them. Since the last ball has no neighbor, it is forced outwards. The number of balls projected depends on the force of the impulse produced.

Variation (see photo on page 45): Make a wooden frame (two boards 40 cm long and two 35 cm long). Insert screw-eyes in wooden croquet balls. Put a thread through each screw-eye and tie it around a board 27 cm wide. Remove the loop thus obtained and place it astride the upper board of the frame. Put the balls side by side touching each other and fix the threads in place with glue.

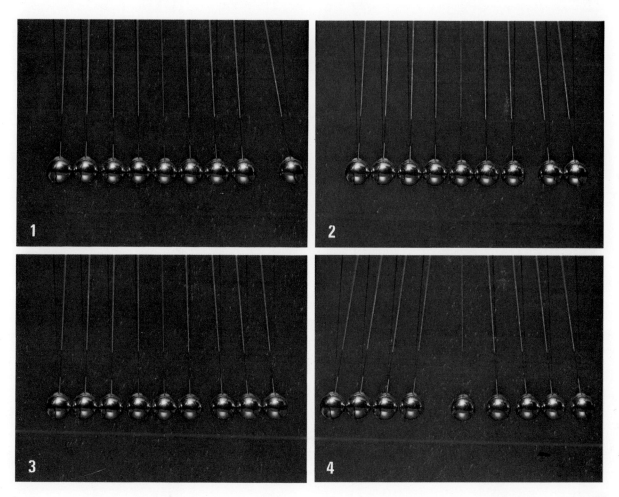

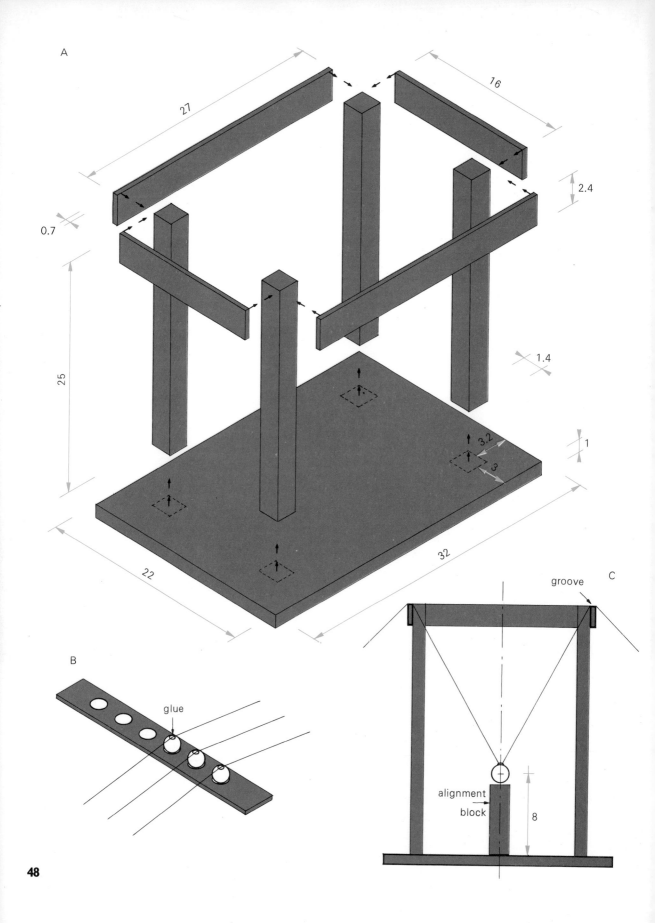

A

27

16

2.4

0.7

25

1.4

3.2

3

1

22

32

B

glue

C

groove

alignment

block

8

48

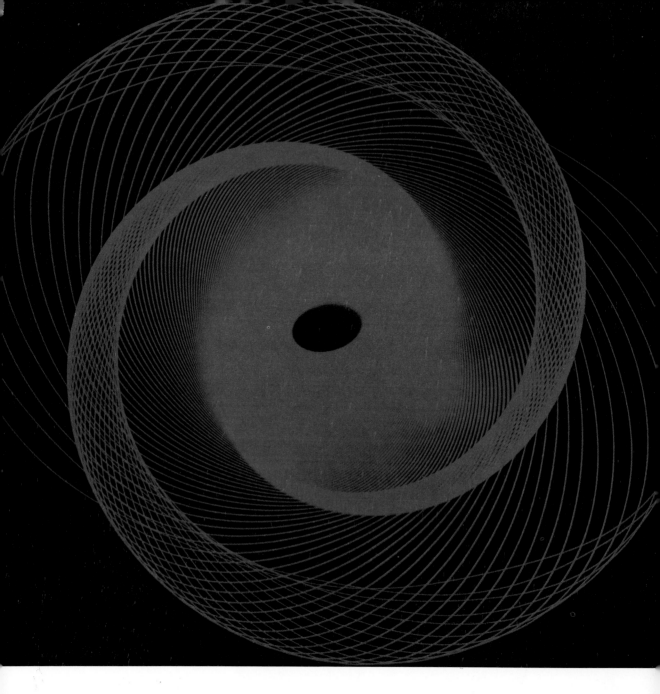

Pendulum of light

or how to record the path of a luminous pendulum

Supplies: flashlight; colored varnish (housewares shop); disc of black paper; iron wire; camera and color film, if possible.

Dip the flashlight bulb in the varnish, let excess drip off and let it dry. With iron wire make a rigid handle at the base of the flashlight. Remove the lens from the flashlight and cover the reflector with the black paper. Hang a string from the ceiling and tie the flashlight to it, 1.7 meters from the floor (see drawing on page 50). Place the camera on the floor directly under the flashlight (use a plumb line

for precision). Set the distance on the camera at about 1.7 meters and adjust the diaphragm accordingly. If your film is 160 or 125 ASA set it at 22; for 80 or 64 ASA, at 16; for 50 ASA, at 11; for 25 ASA at 8. The exact exposure will depend on the flashlight, so experiment with a variety of diaphragm openings. Turn the lights off, light the flashlight and push in a circular motion. Open the shutter (B exposure, or use a locking cable release). When the flashlight stops moving, close the shutter. Your picture will look like the one above. By hanging the flashlight with two or three strings, you will get images like Photos 1 and 2 on page 50.

49

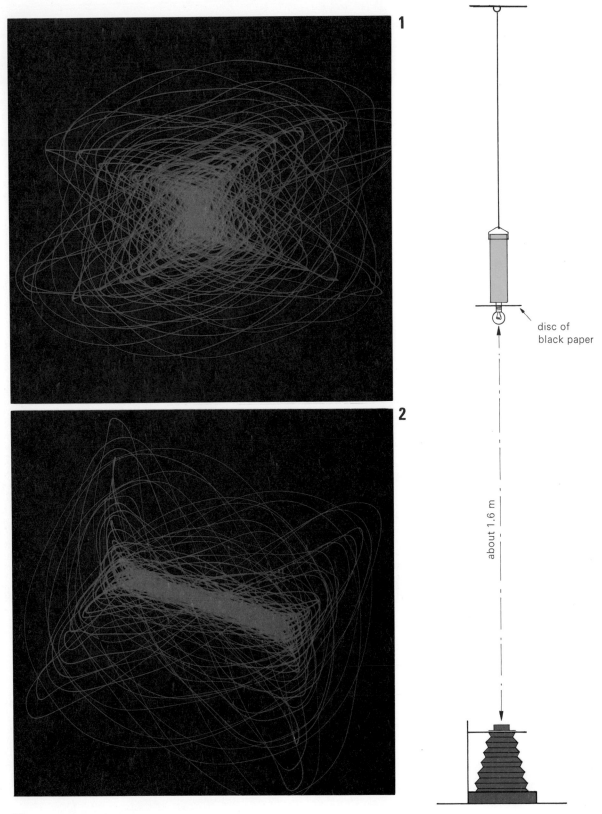

disc of
black paper

about 1.6 m

Balancing tricks

despite appearances, these arrangements stay in balance without recourse to witchcraft

Supplies: bottle with metal cap; two ordinary forks; one dessert fork; pencil; one large cork and one flat cork; one metal knitting needle; wooden clothespin.

Photo 1. Shove a knitting needle through the large cork and stick two forks in it, one on each side, as shown in the photo. Place the base of the needle on the metal cap of the bottle. To keep this assembly balanced, you have to stick the forks fairly deep in the cork and keep them at the same angle.

Photo 2. Place the large cork on the edge of the table. Stick a pencil through the flat cork and stick a dessert fork into the cork. Attach a clothespin to the handle of the fork. Put the tip of the pencil on the large cork. To balance this assembly, ease the flat cork back and forth on the pencil. The corks used in both this and the previous experiment can be replaced by a potato or modelling clay.

Many experiments of this sort are possible. Try to think up other simple ones using common objects.

☐ The force of gravity pulls vertically, from top to bottom. It is at work in our constructions, and is concentrated at a point called the center of gravity. If this point is on a vertical with the point of suspension, above it or below it, the assembly will not fall. The two forks in the first experiment play the part of the balancing pole used by tightrope walkers to keep their equilibrium on the rope.

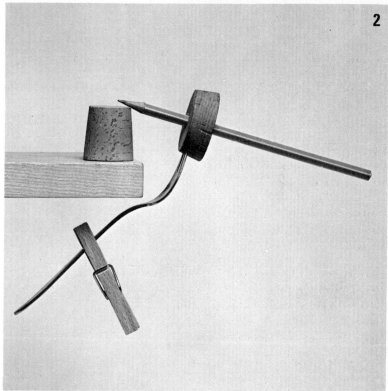

light

The electric company

model lighting system for streets and houses

Supplies: 7 small light bulbs without bases and one 6-volt battery (if not available, use 7 ordinary 3.5 volt lamps and one 4.5 volt battery); 2 metres of ordinary flexible electric wire stripped of its casing (cut the casing along the entire length of the wire); light wires (for an electric bell); the wrapper for an ordinary household light bulb; a box and the cardboard containers for two bulbs; adhesive tape;

seven wooden spools; seven pencils or dowels; seven brads; length of rigid electric wire; board two metres long; wood glue; adhesive tape; small nails.

Construct the seven line towers, following Drawing A on page 56. Sandpaper all sawed surfaces. Build the little house according to the plans shown in Drawings B and C on pages 56 and 57 using the carton of a light bulb.

To make each window, make one vertical cut in the cardboard and two horizontal cuts at top and bottom of the

vertical cut, then open out the shutters. The bulb is inserted through a hole made in the box and two small wires (for an electric bell) connect it to the top pole. The latter is made from a rigid electric wire partially stripped of its casing, bent with two right angles and attached to the inside wall by a piece of adhesive tape. Fasten the towers along the main axis of the board with glue. The electric generator, the battery, goes at one end of the board and the house is glued near the other end (this arrangement is easier to set up than the layout shown in the photo).

Untwist the flexible wire after stripping it and make two

cables, each composed of three strands of wire twisted together. Attach the first one to one of the electric bell wires on the top pole of the house, then wind it twice around one of the nails in the first tower. Make the wire quite taut, then continue in the same way with the other towers and attach the end to one of the terminals of the battery. Do the same with the second wire. Open out the two wires of the small bulbs and place them across the wires of the towers: they will light up immediately.

If you only have bulbs with bases, make little holders for them like those in the photo and Drawing D on page 57.

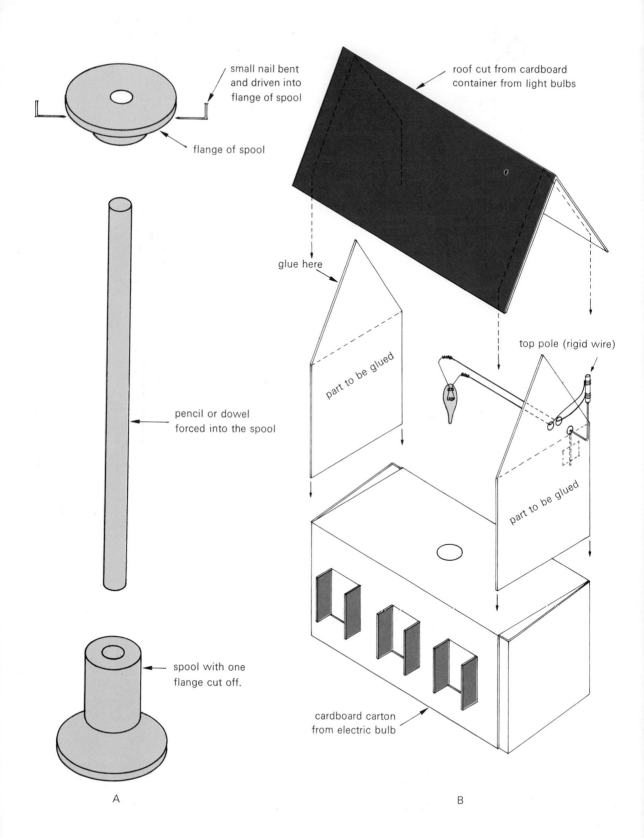

small nail bent and driven into flange of spool

flange of spool

roof cut from cardboard container from light bulbs

pencil or dowel forced into the spool

glue here

part to be glued

top pole (rigid wire)

part to be glued

spool with one flange cut off.

cardboard carton from electric bulb

A

B

C

cardboard carton

roof

roof support

width of the box

D

strips of metal, cardboard and paper are 1.5 cm wide

6.5-cm strip of heavy paper

6-cm strip of metal

6-cm strip of cardboard

3.7-cm strip of metal

flashlight bulb

drill hole for bulb through short strip of metal—bulb should screw in

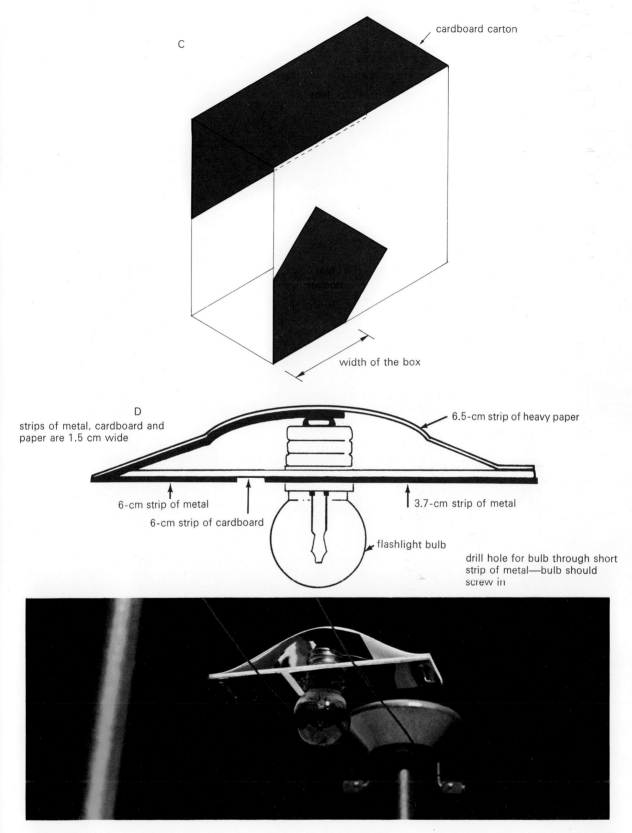

The luminous fountain

Supplies: 1-litre plastic bottle; cork to fit bottle; two small tubes; two lengths of flexible tubing, one 50 cm long, one 1 m long; glass medicine dropper; pocket flashlight; plastic foam ice container; pieces of plastic foam; wood glue; flexible wire grill or fencing; iron wire; mercurochrome.

To make the elevated reservoir, use scissors to cut the bottom from a plastic bottle. Put a hole in the cork and place the cork in the mouth of the bottle. Next fit the 50-cm tube into one of the small tubes and insert it into the cork. Make a 50-cm-high cylinder out of the wire grill, with about the same diameter as the bottle. To hold it in shape, twist the cut wire ends of one edge round the other edge. Insert the reservoir into the cylinder and fix it in place with the iron wire.

To make the fountain, follow the drawing below. Use a knife to cut out several thicknesses of plastic foam. Leave an opening in the middle and place half an ice container over it. Use wood glue to hold the parts together. Then insert the medicine dropper, connected to the reservoir tube. Insert the long tube into the other pipe and insert this into the bottom of the tank. This is the drainage tube and should empty into a pail placed at a lower level. Paint the housing of the flashlight black. Turn the lights off in the room, light the flashlight and fill the tank with water tinted with a few drops of mercurochrome. A luminous jet of water spurts up and falls into the container, from which it drains into the pail.

□ The light is propagated through the jet but cannot escape from it. The placement of the reservoir higher than the fountain causes the water to spurt by itself.

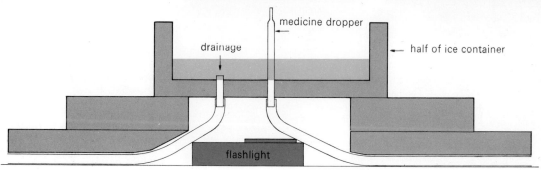

medicine dropper

drainage

← half of ice container

flashlight

59

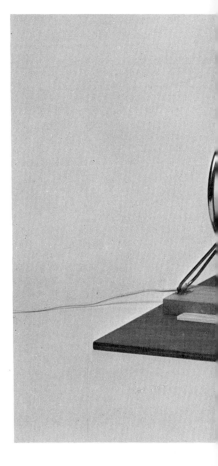

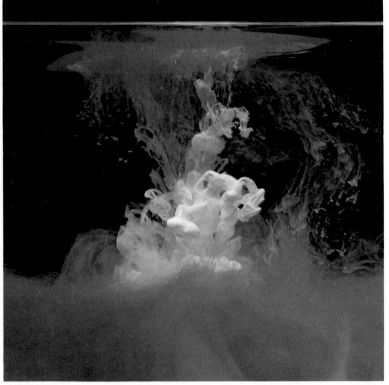

Multi-purpose projector

for transparencies, microprojection, animated projection, etc.

Supplies: 86 × 31 cm board; wooden strip 2.5 × 1.5 cm and 1.5 m long; corrugated cardboard carton; two blocks of wood, one 7 × 10 cm, the other 7 × 16 cm; thick square of cardboard 30 × 30 cm; magnifying glass; *for the slide,* small board 12 × 20 cm, wooden strip 2.5 × 1.5 cm and 33 cm long, two glass plates 10 × 10 cm and two plastic-coated steel clothespins or metal clamps; *for the condenser,* a spherical glass container (small goldfish bowl, carafe, etc.) or if not available, a cylindrical vase; lamp fixture with socket and plug; magnifying mirror; metal clamp; frosted light bulb (60W); wood screws; metal washers; silicone glue; nails.

The different elements of your installation are to be mounted on the wood blocks and placed between strips of wood nailed to the base (as shown in the drawing on page 62) so that they can slide back and forth. Mount the lamp fixture on the larger block with wood screws. Fix the mirror in place behind the bulb as shown using the small clamp.

The axis of projection is along an imaginary horizontal line through the center of the bulb, and the mid-points of the other components must be located on this axis. Make two parallel saw cuts across the smaller block of wood and insert the cardboard square. In the cardboard, on the axis of projection, make a hole slightly smaller than the magnifying glass and fasten the glass in place by glueing on two small cardboard flaps. For the slide holder, mount the wood strip to the small board. Attach clothespins or clamps to the upright with wood screws and washers. Set up the condenser so that its center is on the axis of projection. Use blocks of wood or a cardboard tube to achieve the proper height. Then fill the vessel with water.

Cover the mirror, the lamp and the condenser with a large cardboard box. Make an opening about 10 cm in diameter in front of the condenser and some holes for air intake near the bottom and for ventilation on the top. Cover the air holes with rectangles of cardboard placed on pieces of cork or cardboard so that air can flow but little light escapes (see photo on page 62).

To determine the right place for the glass plates, put a piece of white cardboard in the holder and move it back and forth in front of the light until you obtain an even luminous spot equal in size to the object to be projected. Put the object between the glass plates and install them in the clothespins. Then move the cardboard holding the magnifying glass back and forth to adjust the sharpness of the image projected on a white surface.

This apparatus is wonderful for projecting and enlarging crystals (Photo 1). Dissolve 10 grams of urea (from a pharmacist) in a very small amount of water. Apply the solution with a cotton swab to the surface of the glass and let the water evaporate. Transparencies, microscopic preparations (use a watchmaker's glass as a lens), in fact anything transparent and thin enough to be put between the glass plates—a leaf, for example (photo on page 62) can be projected. You can also make fascinating animated projections by making a "flat aquarium." To do this, apply a thick coat of silicone glue on three edges of both glass plates held 5 mm apart by a piece of cardboard. The cardboard should be smaller than the plates and should stick up above the unjoined side (so that it can be removed). Hold the plates together with two clothespins. Wipe off the edges of the plates with 90° alcohol. You can project some water taken from a puddle, or different colors of gouache paint falling into the water (Photo 2) by pouring these through a small funnel.

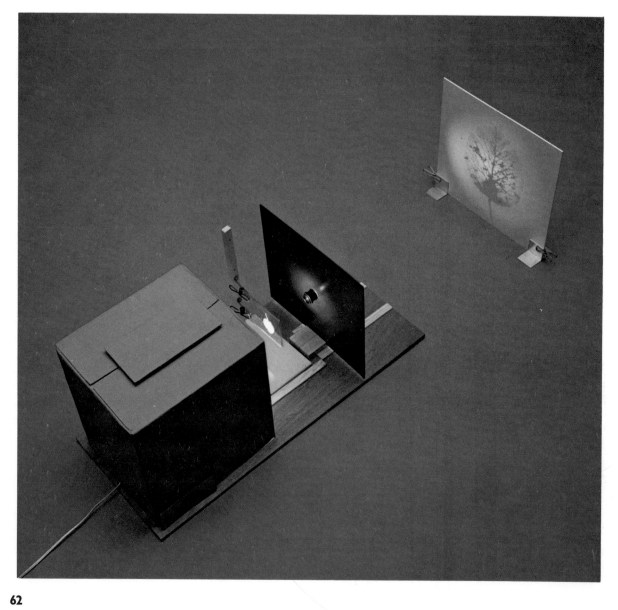

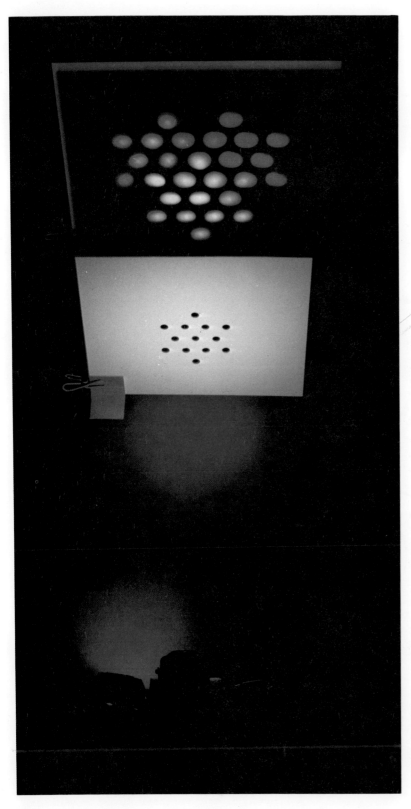

The colors of white light

or how to obtain white light with three colored lights

Supplies: 26 × 28 cm cardboard; a 1-cm punch (or a thick metal tube with a filed edge); three flashlights; pieces of red, blue and green Cellophane®; sheet of white paper; two angle irons; clothespin; elastic bands.

Draw the design below on the cardboard, 7 cm from the bottom, then pierce the holes with the punch. Attach the pieces of Cellophane® to the flashlights with the elastic bands—one of each color. Fasten a sheet of white paper to the wall. At a distance of 25 cm from the sheet, set up the perforated cardboard in a vertical position with the angle irons held by a clothespin. Place the flashlights on the axis 40 cm from the cardboard. The middle one is put on a base, with the other two on each side of it. Turn off the room lights and light the flashlights one after the other in order to adjust the positions of the three beams. All three overlap in the middle (the mixture creates white light) and in pairs on each side (the mixtures give yellow, violet and peacock blue).

The result of your experiment will be even more spectacular than the photograph.

□ White light is actually composed of green, blue and red rays. These three colors are called additive primaries. The two-by-two mixture of light gives the secondary colors, yellow, magenta and cyan.

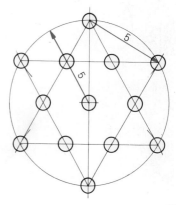

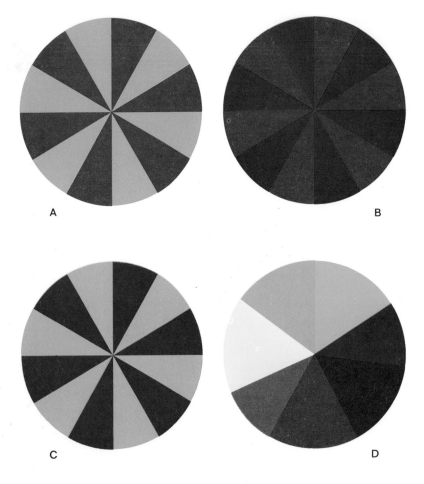

A

B

C

D

Colored tops

Supplies: clockworks or wooden spools with round sticks or dowels; cardboard; colored soft-tipped pens.

To make a top from a spool, saw one of the flanges off and force a piece of dowel into the hole, having first sharpened one of the dowel ends in a pencil sharpener. If the dowel is too loose, wrap some adhesive tape round it. Reproduce the discs at the left on the cardboard and place them on the tops. When you spin them, disc A will appear yellow, disc B, violet, disc C, peacock blue, and disc D, white.

☐ Our eyes perceive the mixture of colors only. Newton's disc (D) makes it possible to reproduce the synthesis of white light.

Paths of light

Supplies: solution of mercurochrome in alcohol (see "Luminescent liquid" below); glass; piece of black cardboard with four holes, each 1 cm in diameter.

Fill the glass or a larger container with the solution and place it in full sunlight. Place the cardboard in front of the glass, as shown in Photo 1. The light that penetrates the glass forms two linear beams emanating from the two lower holes (the light is propagated in a straight line). The light coming through the third hole, striking the surface of the liquid, bends towards the vertical—this is the phenomenon called refraction.

Luminescent liquid

Supplies: mercurochrome; fuel alcohol; glass; blotting paper.

Mix several drops of mercurochrome in the alcohol. Let stand for 48 hours. Decant and filter through blotting paper. Put the solution in a glass illuminated by sunlight. Depending on the angle from which you look at it, the liquid will appear either red or green and orange (see the glass on the left in both Photos 2 and 3). The glasses on the right contain fluorescein dissolved in ammonia heavily diluted with water.

☐ If we subjected these liquids to black light (ultraviolet rays), they would glow. This is the phenomenon called fluorescence.

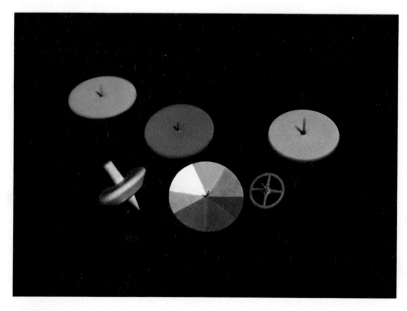

The city of light

it shines, it lives, the light runs from one building to another, just as in a real city

Supplies: sheet of cardboard 70 × 35 cm; 22 small matchboxes; 22 3.5 V bulbs; three 4.5 V batteries all connected positive to positive and negative to negative; flexible electric wire in two different colors; foil; cardboard 19 × 12 cm; round-head paper fasteners; round-head nails; strip of wood 10 cm long; washers; 4-mm punch; thumbtacks, glue; cork.

Reproduce the grid from the drawing below on cardboard. Mark places for the holes and matchboxes. Then draw around them, any way that you prefer, the silhouette of a city. Cut out the silhouette with a knife and pierce holes with the punch.

The layout of the wiring is shown in Drawing A. To hold the lights in place, use method B or C. For method B, screw the lights into the matchbox drawer and glue all the boxes to the cardboard (see drawing this page). With a completely stripped wire (blue wire in Drawing A), wire all the bases together, looping the wire twice around each bulb and passing it between the drawer and the case of each matchbox. Connect end to battery. Strip the ends of a red wire and attach one end to the first matchbox case with a paper fastener. Assemble the matchbox drawer and case so that the paper fastener is in good contact with the contact stud of the bulb. Attach the other end of the wire to one of the paper fasteners of the control panel (Drawing D). Connect each bulb the same way.

For method C, connect all the bulbs (screwed into matchbox drawers) with blue wire stripped completely. The end goes to the battery. Next strip the end of a red wire, make a loop and attach it to the side of one matchbox under a foil strip (6.5 x 1 cm). The foil should be stapled to both sides of the box, passing across the contact stud of the bulb. The other end of the red wire is attached with a paper fastener to the control panel. After the wiring of the first box is completed, glue the box to the cardboard. Proceed in the same way with all the other boxes.

Fasten the control panel to a base and make the switch as shown in Drawing E. Connect the red wire of the switch to the battery. By turning the switch, the city lights up in different places. The photo on page 66 shows a wiring set-up for lighting the whole city at once. The bases of the bulbs and the foil strips are connected to each other, then to the battery. The red cardboard pieces are to be glued to the white cutout to keep it upright.

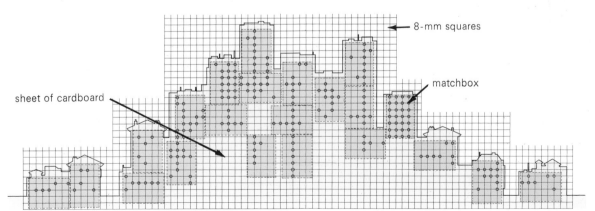

8-mm squares

matchbox

sheet of cardboard

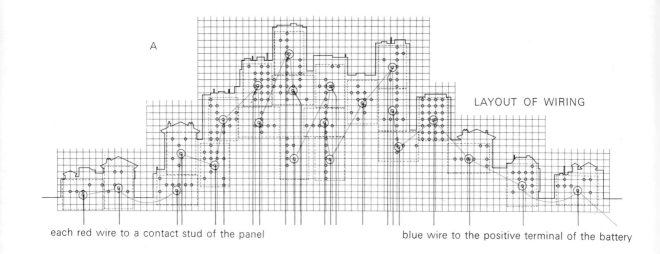

A

LAYOUT OF WIRING

each red wire to a contact stud of the panel

blue wire to the positive terminal of the battery

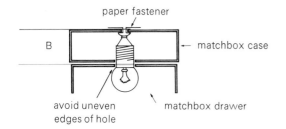

paper fastener

B

matchbox case

avoid uneven edges of hole

matchbox drawer

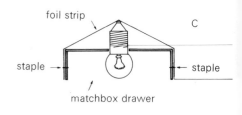

foil strip

C

staple

staple

matchbox drawer

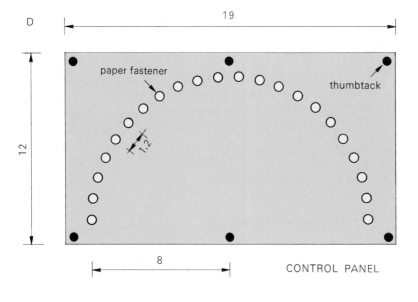

D

19

paper fastener

thumbtack

1,2

12

8

CONTROL PANEL

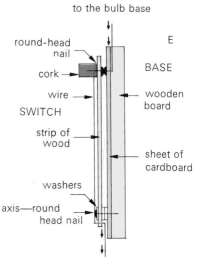

to the bulb base

round-head nail

E

cork

BASE

wire

wooden board

SWITCH

strip of wood

sheet of cardboard

washers

axis—round head nail

to the negative terminal of the battery

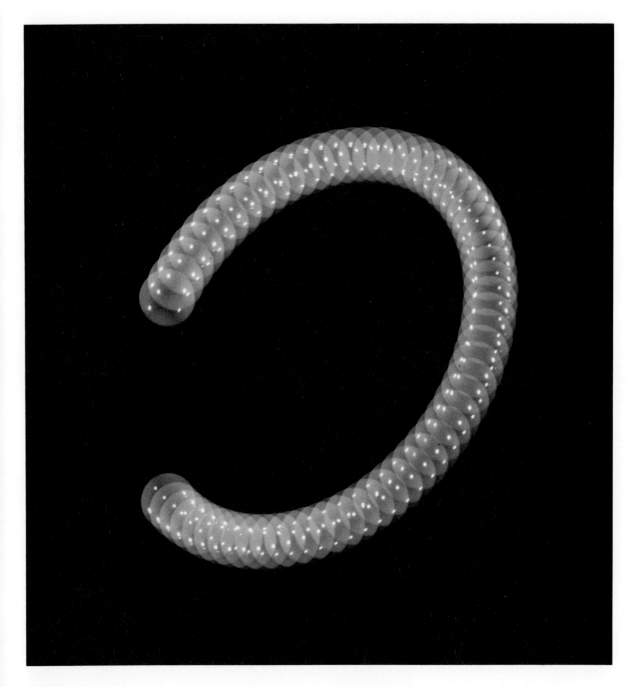

Stroboscopy

seeing phenomena invisible to the naked eye

Stroboscopy is a fascinating means of studying and observing phenomena that repeat at regular intervals too fast for the eye to record. For example, the stroboscope enables us to see the blades of an electric fan in motion, and many other equally spectacular things, as we shall see later.

Supplies: sheet of cardboard (laminated, if possible); wooden spool (sawed in half); pencil or dowel; thumbtack or upholstery tack; washer; wood glue; black paint; soap or a candle.

On the cardboard, trace the outline of a disc with slots (drawing on page 71), then cut it out. The slots are opened

up with a knife. Glue half a spool to the middle of the disc with wood glue (or two thumbtacks). Paint the whole thing black. Put a hole in the middle of the disc and insert a tack with a washer. Put the pencil (smeared with soap or candlewax) in the hole of the spool and force the tack into it. To make the device work, hold the disc in front of your eyes in one hand and spin it with the other hand. Here are some things to observe: the circular trajectory of a ball hung from a string (photo page 69), a saw blade vibrating, a long strip of wood shaking, the rings of the wave tank (page 79), the colored tops (page 64), the blades of an electric fan, a bicycle wheel, etc. If you turn the disc at the same speed as the bicycle wheel, the wheel will appear motionless. If you turn it slower than the wheel, the wheel will appear to move slowly. If you turn it faster, the wheel will appear to move slowly but in the reverse of its real direction. You can also distinguish each drop of water in the fountain on page 59, for what seems to be a jet is actually a succession of drops. A camera aimed through the revolving disc will record the trajectory of a painted table-tennis ball (see photos on this page).

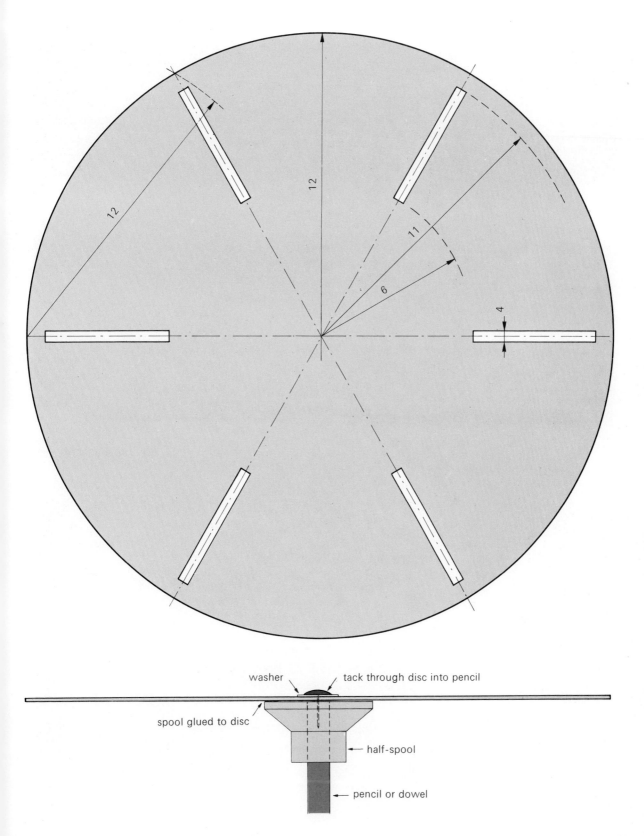

washer   tack through disc into pencil

spool glued to disc

half-spool

pencil or dowel

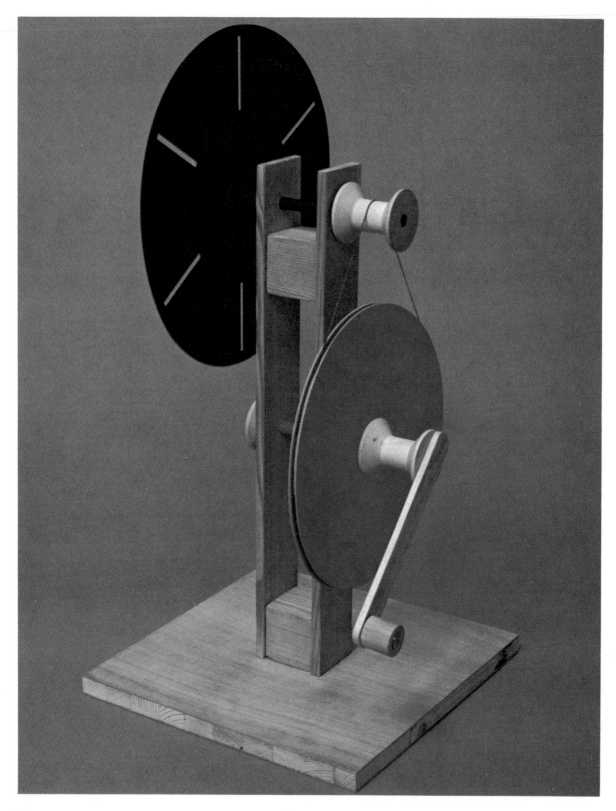

Improved stroboscope

a more precise device that will give you the ability to extend your observations, especially of very rapid phenomena

Supplies: two children's cubic wooden blocks; two flat strips of wood of the same width as the cubes and 36 cm long; four wooden spools; three cardboard circles (two with a diameter of 20 cm and one with a diameter of 19 cm); one cardboard disc with a diameter of 24 cm; two pencils or dowels that can be squeezed into the spools; one wooden strip 15 × 2 cm; one board 24 × 24 × 1.5 cm; wood glue; small nails; one wood screw; one thumbtack; one large elastic band; candlewax or soap.

You will find a detailed drawing of the construction of this apparatus on page 74. The disc is the same as the one on page 71. To saw the spools more easily, put a piece of dowelling through the hole. To smooth off the cut edges, you will have better control if you put your spool on top of another one and shove a pencil through both. Coat the inside of the holes that you make with soap or candlewax. If there is any play between the spool and the dowel, wrap adhesive tape around the dowel, and if necessary, drive a small nail through the spool and the dowel to hold them together. The belt (elastic band) should not be too tight on the pulleys.

Stroboscopic lighting device

The photo above and the drawing at the right show how to build a lighting device with a block of the same dimensions as those used previously and two pieces of wood of the same width as the block. The little nails in the block serve as supports: there are two in front and two in back. The large nail can be pulled out easily and serves to hold the flashlight.

In a dark room, turn the disc with the handle and illuminate a colored top (page 64). If you look directly at the top, it will appear motionless. Try looking at other moving objects the same way.

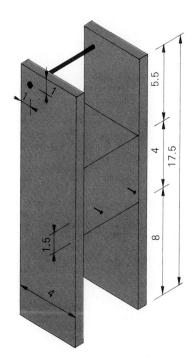

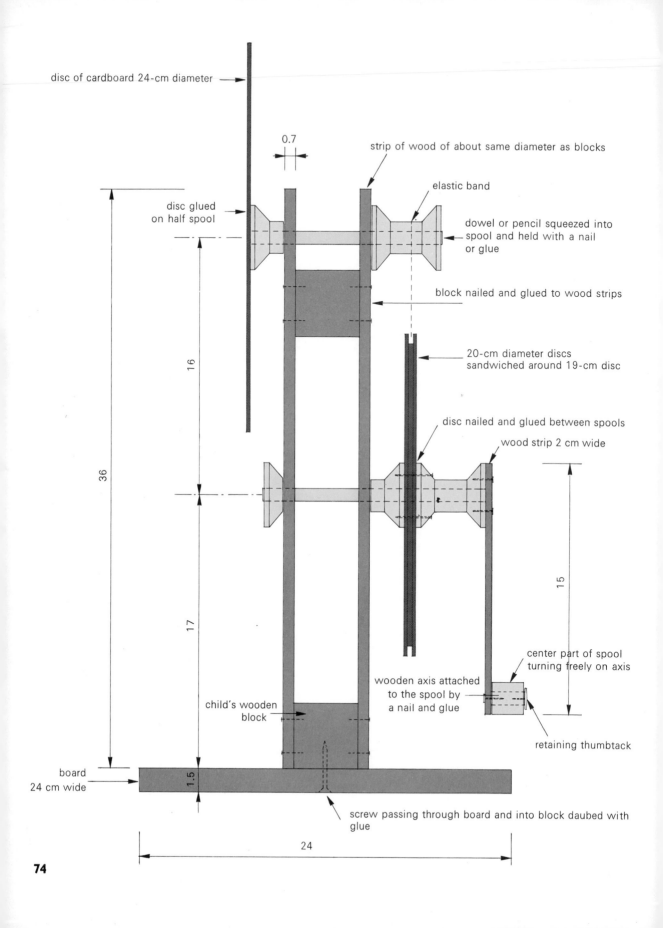

disc of cardboard 24-cm diameter

0.7

strip of wood of about same diameter as blocks

elastic band

disc glued
on half spool

dowel or pencil squeezed into
spool and held with a nail
or glue

block nailed and glued to wood strips

20-cm diameter discs
sandwiched around 19-cm disc

16

disc nailed and glued between spools

wood strip 2 cm wide

36

15

17

center part of spool
turning freely on axis

child's wooden
block

wooden axis attached
to the spool by
a nail and glue

retaining thumbtack

board
24 cm wide

1.5

screw passing through board and into block daubed with
glue

24

A rainbow

Supplies: smooth-sided drinking glass; water; large sheet of white paper.

When the sun is fairly low in the sky, either in the morning or the evening, place a glass of water on a window-sill in full sunlight. Fill the glass with water to the brim and place a large piece of white paper on the floor near the window, just touching the wall. You will see a magnificent rainbow containing all the colors of the solar spectrum. In the photo, this experiment was done by placing a small table in front of a doorway.

Variation: Put a basin full of water in full sunlight and place a rectangular pocket mirror against the inside of the basin, directed towards the sun. Then tilt it—the solar spectrum appears overhead on the ceiling.

Variation: Early in the morning or at the end of a sunny day, turn on the spray of a garden hose and stand in front of some dark foliage with your back to the sun. You will see a rainbow.

☐ This phenomenon is called dispersion of light. The rim of the glass of water, the angle of the glass in the basin, the drops of water in the spray, play the role of a prism and break up the light. The white light of the sun is in fact formed by the mixture of an infinity of colored rays, as these experiments show.

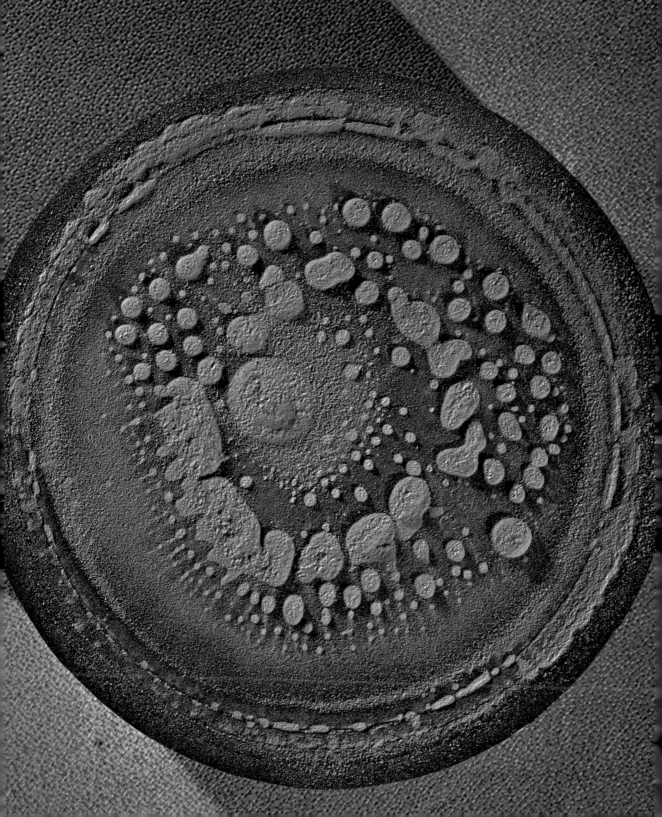

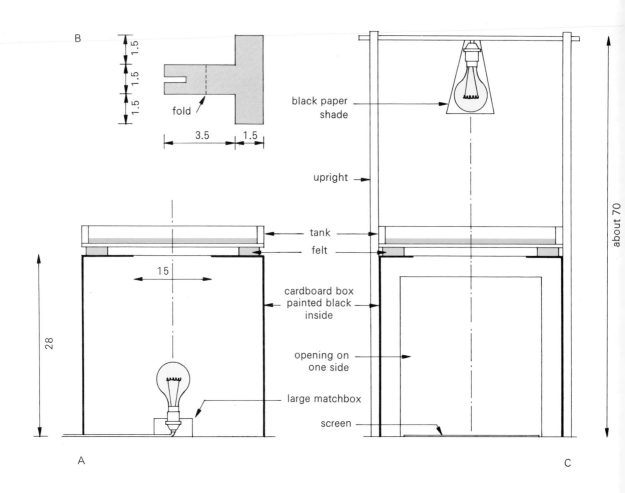

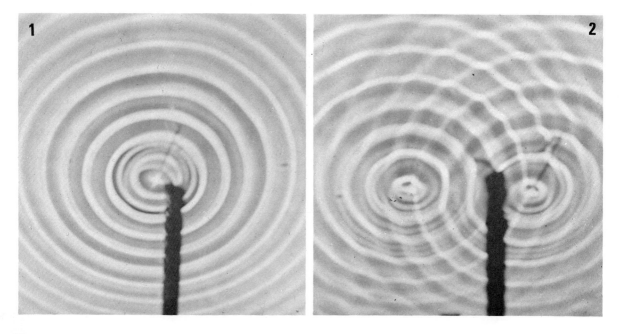

B

1.5
1.5
1.5
1.5

fold

3.5   1.5

black paper
shade

upright

tank

felt

15

cardboard box
painted black
inside

28

opening on
one side

large matchbox

screen

about 70

A

C

1

2

Circles in the water

or how sound waves are propagated

Supplies: corrugated cardboard cartons about 25 × 25 cm and 28 to 30 cm high; glass plate 25 × 25 cm; modelling clay; strip of felt; large matchbox; electric socket with cord and plug; clear light bulb (60 W); holder (see page 61); hacksaw blade; brass wire; piece of tin plate; metal screw and nut; piece of wood 4 × 4 × 1.5 cm; two wood screws; matte black paint.

Cut a circular opening 15 cm in diameter in the top of the box and remove the flaps from the bottom. Paint the inside of the box black. Mount the lamp socket in the large matchbox (Drawing A). Next make a wall of modelling clay 1.5 cm high around the edge of the glass plate. The inside surface of the wall should slope somewhat and the clay should fit firmly on the glass. Place two strips of felt on each side of the opening of the box and put the glass plate on top of them with the clay wall facing up.

Make a saw cut in the 4 x 4-cm block of wood 2.5 cm long, 1 cm from the edge. Attach the block to the holder with a screw and pass the metal saw blade through the cut, holding it in place with a wood screw. Bend a thick brass

wire 2.5 cm long to form a right angle. Attach it to the blade by making a loop to hold a metal screw and a washer. Place the holder near the glass plate and put a weight on the base of the holder. The end of the brass wire should descend vertically into the tank but should not touch the bottom. Fill the tank with water up to a height of from 5 to 8 mm.

Turn off the room lights and flick the free end of the saw with your finger. You will see shadows of circular ripples form on the ceiling, originating at the wire and spreading out in the tank. These are continuous waves that move like sound waves (Photo 1). Now attach another bent brass wire next to the first one, keeping the tips separated by 5 cm or more. Note the new pattern that forms (Photo 2). Here we have the phenomenon of interference of waves. Replace the brass wire with a little T-shaped piece of tinplate (see Drawing B), and you will produce rectilinear waves. This arrangement will enable you to conduct a lot of other experiments. Try, for example, putting obstacles of various shapes in the water and observe how the waves are reflected or changed. Drawing C offers a variation of the set-up. Here the waves are projected below the tank and you will get much sharper images.

79

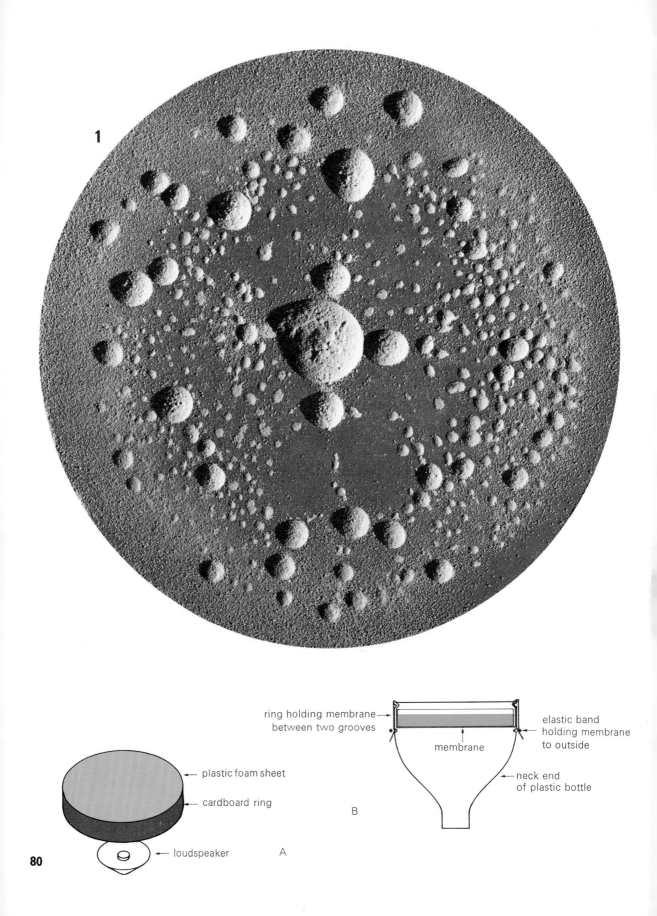

1

ring holding membrane
between two grooves

membrane

elastic band
holding membrane
to outside

neck end
of plastic bottle

B

plastic foam sheet

cardboard ring

loudspeaker

A

Music for the eyes

Supplies: plastic bottles with caps; strong tissue paper or Cellophane®; flexible plastic tube for electrical installations; nylon sheet (packing bag); ring of cardboard 10 cm high; sheet of plastic foam; corks; sandpaper; powder shaker.

Stretch a piece of tissue paper over the cardboard ring and hold it in place with an elastic band, or glue a sheet of plastic foam onto the edge of the ring (Photo 2 at right and Drawing A). Rub some cork on the sandpaper and put the powder obtained in the shaker. Place the membrane on the loudspeaker of a record player set up nearby and sprinkle powdered cork evenly over the membrane. Put a record on the player and turn up the volume. Immediately the powder begins to dance and to distribute itself across the membrane forming a pattern corresponding to the sounds which make it vibrate (Photos 1 and 3). Each musical phrase has a distinct image of its own (spread the powder each time).

To make the "sound pipe" (Photo 2, right), cut the neck end from a plastic bottle, keeping a groove for rigidity. Sand the cut edge until smooth and attach a membrane as before. Cut the center of the cap and fit a bent tube into it. Sprinkle the membrane with cork and pronounce a vowel sound loudly, holding the sound, into the end of the tube. Heaps of powder appear, forming a different pattern for each vowel (respread the powder each time). You will also get interesting patterns by applying a thin film of milk to a nylon membrane stretched over the "sound pipe" (Drawing B). A ring cut in the bottle is shortened by 5 mm and the ends stapled. It squeezes the membrane between two grooves.

Variation: Substitute powdered copper for the cork. You will see quite different patterns.

☐ Powder and liquid materialize sound waves hitting the membrane and let us "see" what we would normally hear.

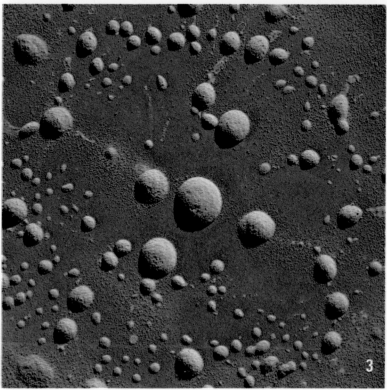

Music without do-re-mi

Even if you don't know the scales, you can make music. Whether by yourself or with friends, you can easily discover some simple musical instruments right around you. Here are some ideas that will put you on the right track (a track of endless exploration).

Musical bottles: Take 5 or 7 identical bottles and fill them with water at different levels. Tap the bottles with wooden mallets.

Gong: Take a round metal tray (or several of different diameters) and put a bent paper clip through the rim. Tie a string to the clip and hang the tray from a support. Make a hammer by putting a thick wad of cotton wool (absorbent cotton) on the end of a stick, wrap it in a piece of cloth and tie all to the stick. Hit the gong in the middle.

Carillon: Get some spiral springs from a junk dealer. Hang them by strings and strike them with wooden mallets or a hammer.

Simplified xylophone: Take some steel tubes (from electrical installations) or tubes of any other metal, or of bamboo or hard wood, of different lengths. Pierce two holes in one end and hang the tubes from a support by strings. Strike them with wooden mallets. Brake drums of different sizes also give excellent results when hung by strings.

Musical pipe: Flatten the end of a plastic straw between your teeth up to a length of 1 cm. With scissors cut the corners of the flattened part. The two flattened sides should be very close but not touching one another. Blow into the straw, taking the entire flattened area between your lips. Make pipes of various lengths—they produce different sounds.

Water trombone: Fill a 1-litre bottle with water. Take a 20-cm-long tube, 1 cm in diameter, open at both ends, and put it fairly far into the bottle. Blow into it, with the upper lip extended. You will get varied sounds.

Sound riddles

Play sound-effects man and make your friends guess what certain sounds are supposed to represent. Here are some examples:

Fire: Crinkle a piece of Cellophane® between your hands.

The cracking of tree trunks during a fire: Break a wooden strawberry box under your feet.

Thunder: Shake a thin sheet of tinplate, holding it by one corner.

Thunder in the mountains: Shake a large sheet of foil (50 x 65 cm).

A boxer's punch: Punch a firm, round head of cabbage.

Horse's hoofbeats: 1. Bang two halves of a coconut shell on pavement or another hard surface. 2. Bang two halves of a coconut shell inside a wooden box or on a piece of cardboard with a thin covering of sand.

Siren of a boat: Blow over the opening of a cylindrical 2-litre can or drum.

Helicopter: Tie a 60-cm-long string to a 40-cm-long ruler. Hold the end of the string and turn the ruler faster and faster in a circle.

The howling tube

Supplies: glass tube 3 cm in diameter open at both ends; metal grill 3 cm in diameter; stiff wire; alcohol lamp with a long neck (take an ink bottle fitted with a pierced cork through which a long metal tube passes, put a hole in the cap of the ink bottle and pass tubes through it, or use a Bunsen burner).

Hang the grill inside the tube exactly 10 cm from the base with two wires whose upper ends are bent back. Place the tube vertically above the flame of the alcohol lamp and heat the grill red hot. When you remove the tube from the flame, a faint mournful howl can be heard.

☐ This is an effect of resonance: the column of air put in motion by the heat of the grill makes the tube vibrate.

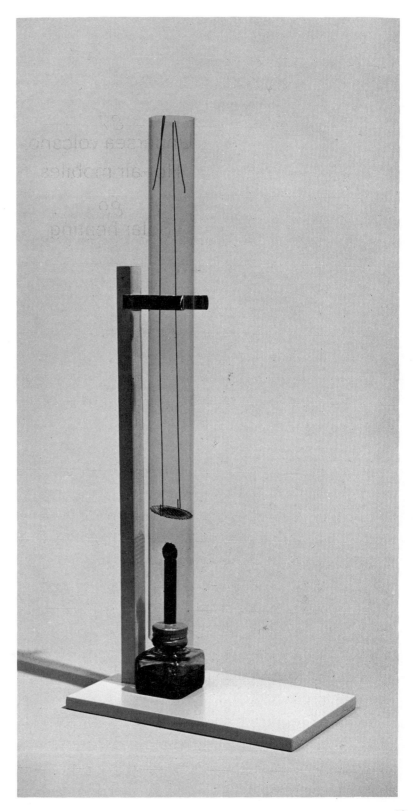

heat

Undersea volcano

or how to see convection currents in water (see photo on page 85)

Supplies: ink bottle; glass medicine dropper tube; small tube; cork; aquarium or large glass container.

Put two holes in the cork to accommodate two tubes; the dropper should be flush with the lower side of the cork and stick up 5 cm; the other tube is flush with the upper side of the cork and extends almost to the bottom of the ink bottle. Fill the aquarium with very cold water and fill the bottle with very hot water tinted with ink. Cover the bottle, wipe off the outside and place it quickly on the floor of the aquarium. The volcano immediately begins to erupt.

☐ Here you are observing convection currents in water. The hot water is lighter than the cold and escapes from the ink bottle and rises while cold water descends and fills the bottle. Central heating in buildings works on this principle.

Hot-air mobiles

Supplies: sheet of foil or drawing paper; fine brass wire; beads.

Reproduce the design below and that on page 91. If you use foil, trace the pattern with a pin. After you cut out the pattern below, gently twist each blade in the same direction. Make a hole in the middle of each mobile and put a perfectly straight brass wire through it. Attach one end of the wire to a support and attach a bead to the other end. The mobile should rest lightly on the bead. Hang the mobiles above a source of heat (radiator, electric lamp, candle, etc.) and they will begin to turn rapidly.

Variation: Make foil mobiles, but do not pierce the middles. Instead, lightly push a pencil into the middle of each to make a little dent. Place your mobiles on top of knitting needles (or sharp pencils) stuck into spools and put them on the radiator. The rising currents of hot air will turn the mobiles.

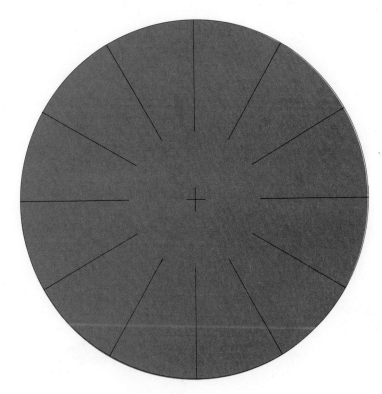

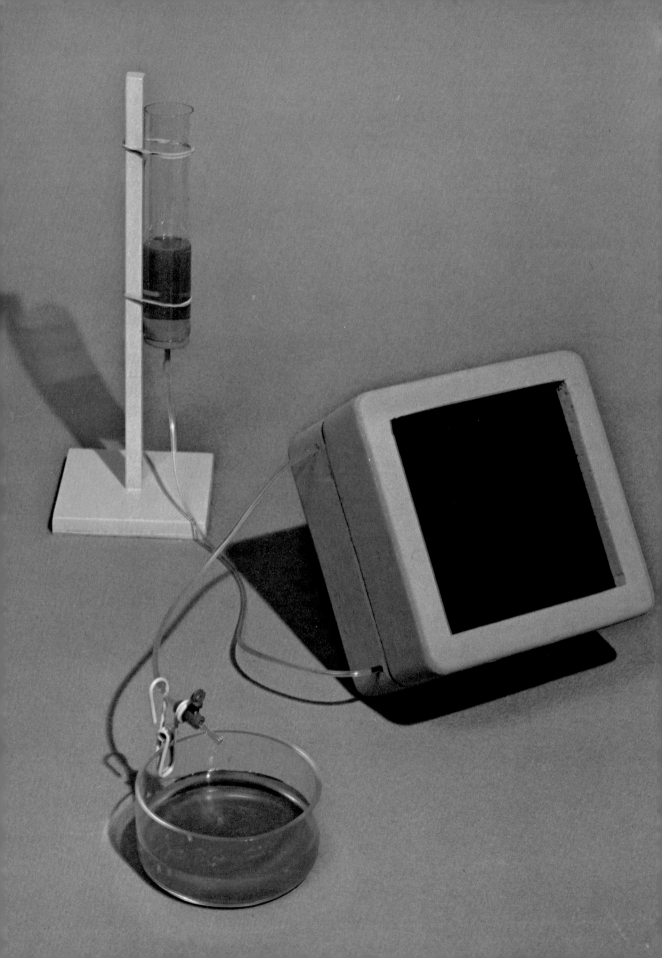

Solar heating

or how to use the sun around the house

**Supplies: plastic foam ice container; glass plate
and aluminum sheet that just fit inside the container; aluminum tubing 1 m long and about 5 mm
in diameter (from a supplier of model supplies);
thick glass tube open at both ends or plastic bottle
with bottom cut off; two lengths of flexible tubing;
elastic bands; clothespin; small tubes; cork; matte
black paint; small strips of wood; bowl.**

Construct the receiver following Drawings A and B on page
90 and the photo above. Bend the aluminum tube in the
shape shown without flattening it. You can do this by
bending it around the thread of a small screw-top bottle
or by pushing it into a coil spring that it just fits into and then
bending. Place the tube on the aluminum sheet and attach
it by making two or three small holes in the sheet with a
nail on each side of the tube. Pass a bit of brass wire through
and twist it under the plate. Paint the plate and tube very
dull (matte) black.

Make a hole in the cork and insert one end of a piece of
flexible tubing. The other end of the tube is attached to one
end of the aluminum heating tube. The other end of the
heating tube is connected to the other piece of flexible
tubing and this runs to the collection dish (bowl). The end
of the tube running to the bowl is furnished with a turn-off
valve (clothespin).

Turn the receiver towards the sun, fill the tank with water
and open the valve to fill the heater. Close the valve,
wait a while, and then open it again. The water in the
heater boils quickly, and this can be repeated until all the
water in the tank is heated.

☐ The glass plate allows sunlight to enter but does not
let heat escape. This is known as the greenhouse effect.
The black heating plate absorbs heat and transmits it to the
tube, which heats the water.

Variation: The drawing below shows the same apparatus
in simplified form.

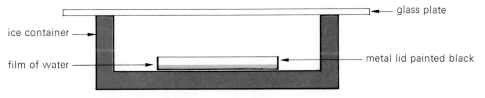

glass plate

ice container

film of water

metal lid painted black

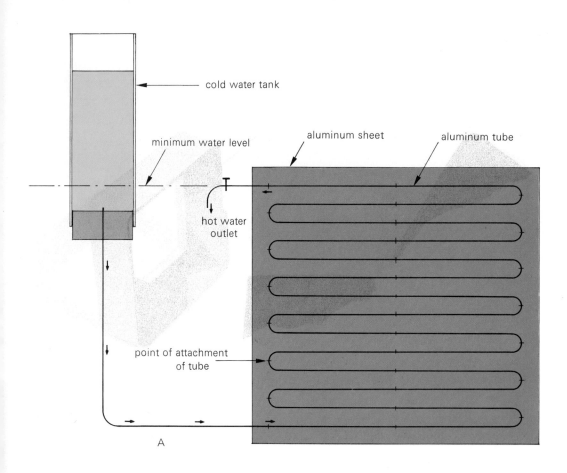

cold water tank

minimum water level

aluminum sheet

aluminum tube

hot water outlet

point of attachment of tube

A

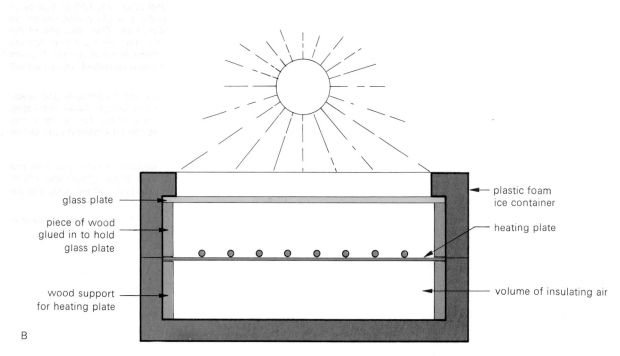

plastic foam ice container

glass plate

heating plate

piece of wood glued in to hold glass plate

wood support for heating plate

volume of insulating air

B

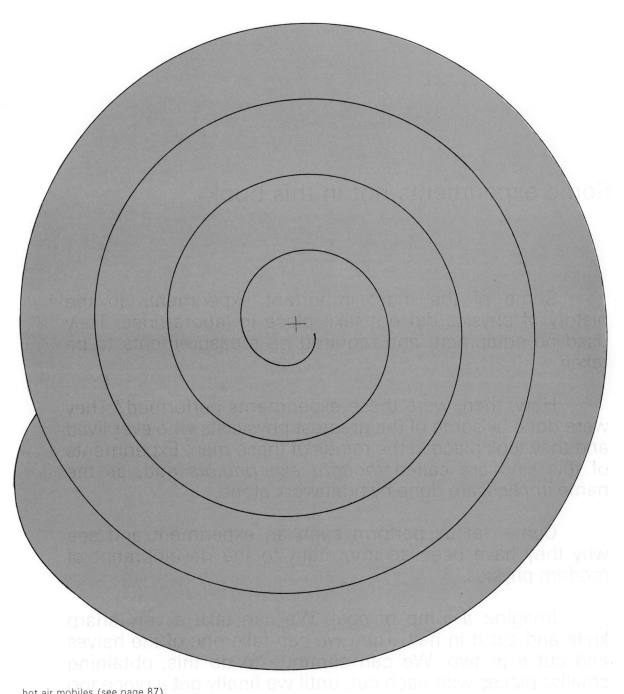

hot air mobiles (see page 87)

Some experiments not in this book

Some of the most important experiments in the history of physics did not take place in laboratories. They used no equipment and required no measurements to be taken.

How, then, were these experiments performed? They were done by some of the greatest physicists who ever lived and they took place in the minds of these men. Experiments of this kind are called *thought experiments* and, as the name implies, are done by brainwork alone.

Come, let us perform such an experiment and see why they have been so important to the development of modern physics.

Imagine a lump of coal. We can take a very sharp knife and cut it in half. Then we can take one of the halves and cut *it* in two. We can continue to do this, obtaining smaller pieces with each cut, until we finally get a piece too small to be cut with our knife. So we get a finer blade and continue the process. Eventually, we will have a piece of coal too small to be cut with any knife, no matter how fine and sharp the blade.

It is said that Democritus of ancient Greece con-
sidered just this. He called the ultimately small piece
atomos, a Greek word meaning "indivisible," the word that
we now know as "atom."

So you see, by thought alone, we have demonstrated
that all matter is composed of atoms. We can further
reason that various substances differ because their atoms
are different.

While this is far from a complete picture, it is the basis
of modern atomic theory. And notice that we didn't use so
much as a ruler!

We must, of course, be careful not to assume that
evidence from thought experiments is conclusive. This can
lead us far astray. For example, Aristotle concluded, by pure
reasoning, that if a 10-kg rock and a 1-kg rock were
dropped, the heavy one would fall ten times as fast as the
light one. It wasn't until centuries later that Galileo showed
otherwise. He reasoned that the rocks would fall at the
same rate, and actually tested his theory. He dropped
objects of different weights from the Leaning Tower of Pisa
and noted that they hit the ground at the same time,
proving that the weight of an object does not determine the
speed at which it falls.

So, as long as we keep in mind that the conclusions
arrived at through thought experiments should not be
accepted completely without physical evidence, there will
be no problems. But also recognize the marvellous things
that can be done by thought alone.

Many of the most brilliant advances of physics started
out as thought experiments. Atomic theory (as we have
seen), relativity, the Uncertainty Principle, quantum theory

and more started out as mere thought and ultimately changed the shape of modern physics and our conception of the universe.

If you follow a career in physics, you may work with balances and spectroscopes, computers and particle accelerators, but you already possess the most important tool that you will ever need. There are countless new discoveries lying in wait for someone to think of them.

Index